W9-DEL-309

Ready, Set, Go!

Cookbook

125 Easy Meals to Get You Started

About ᗑWeight Watchers

Weight Watchers International, Inc., is the world's leading provider of weight-management services, operating globally through a network of company-owned and franchise operations. Weight Watchers holds nearly 50,000 weekly meetings worldwide, at which members receive group support and education about healthful eating patterns, behaviour modification, and physical activity. Weight-loss and weight-management results vary by individual. We recommend that you attend Weight Watchers meetings to benefit from the supportive environment you find there and follow the comprehensive Weight Watchers program, which includes a food plan, an activity plan, and a behavioural component. In addition, Weight Watchers offers a wide range of products, publications, and programs for people interested in weight loss and weight control. For the Weight Watchers meeting nearest you, call **1-800-651-6000**. For information about bringing Weight Watchers to your workplace, call **1-877-AT-WORK1**. Also visit us at our Web site, **WeightWatchers.ca**, and look for *Weight Watchers Magazine* at your newsstand or in your meeting room.

Feta-Stuffed Chicken Breasts, page 99

Weight Watchers Publishing Group

Editorial Director NANCY GAGLIARDI

Creative Director ED MELNITSKY

Production Manager ALAN BIEDERMAN

Photo Editor DEBORAH HARDT

Managing Editor SARAH WHARTON

Editorial Assistant KATERINA GKIONIS

Food Editor EILEEN RUNYAN

Editor DEBORAH MINTCHEFF

Nutrition Consultant PATTY SANTELLI

Photographer ANTONIS ACHILLEOS

Food Stylist JAMIE KIMM

Prop Stylist PAIGE HICKS

Cover Designer DANIELA HRITCU

Art Director PAULINE NEUWIRTH

Copyright © 2011 Weight Watchers International, Inc. Nothing may be reprinted
in whole or in part without permission from the publisher. Editorial and art produced by
W/W Twentyfirst Corp., 11 Madison Avenue, New York, NY 10010.
WEIGHT WATCHERS and *PointsPlus* are registered trademarks of Weight Watchers
International, Inc.
SKU #81200 Printed in the USA

About Our Recipes

While losing weight isn't only about what you eat, Weight Watchers realizes the critical role it plays in your success and overall good health. That's why our philosophy is to offer great-tasting, easy recipes that are nutritious as well as delicious. If you have special dietary needs, consult with your health-care professional for advice on a diet that is best for you and how to adapt these recipes to meet your specific nutritional needs.

To achieve these good-health goals and get the maximum satisfaction from the foods you eat, we suggest you keep the following information in mind while preparing our recipes:

The *PointsPlus*® Program and Good Nutrition

- ▶ Recipes in this book have been developed for Weight Watchers members who are following the *PointsPlus* program. *PointsPlus* values are given for each recipe. They're assigned based on the amount of protein (grams), carbohydrates (grams), fat (grams), and fibre (grams), and alcohol and sugar alcohol (grams), if applicable, contained in a single serving of a recipe.
- ▶ Recipes include approximate nutritional information; they are analysed for Calories (Cal), Total Fat, Saturated Fat (Sat Fat), Trans Fat, Cholesterol (Chol), Sodium (Sod), Total Carbohydrates (Total Carb), Total Sugar, Dietary Fibre (Fib), Protein (Prot), and Calcium (Calc). The nutritional values are calculated by registered dietitians, using nutrition analysis software.
- ▶ Substitutions made to the ingredients will alter the per-serving nutritional information and may affect the *PointsPlus* value.
- ▶ Our recipes meet Weight Watchers Good Health Guidelines for eating lean proteins and fibre-rich whole grains, and having at least five servings of vegetables and fruits and two servings of low-fat or fat-free dairy products a day, while limiting your intake of saturated fat, sugar, and sodium.

- Health agencies recommend an intake of no more than 2300 mg sodium daily. To stay in line with these recommendations we keep sodium levels in our recipes reasonably low; to boost flavour, we often include fresh herbs or a squeeze of citrus instead of salt. If you don't have to restrict your sodium, feel free to add a touch more salt as desired.
- In the recipes a green triangle (▲) indicates Weight Watchers Power Foods.
- Healthy Extra suggestions for adding Power Foods have a *PointsPlus*® value of *0* unless otherwise stated.
- Recipes that work with the Simply Filling technique are listed on page 15. Find more details about this technique at your meeting.
- For more about the science behind lasting weight loss and more, please visit **WeightWatchers.ca/health/sciencecenter.**

PointsPlus value not what you expected?

- You might expect some of the *PointsPlus* values in this book to be lower when some of the foods they're made from, such as fruits and vegetables, have no *PointsPlus* values. Fruit and most veggies have no *PointsPlus* values when served as a snack or part of a meal, like a cup of berries with a sandwich. But if these foods are part of a recipe, their fiber and nutrient content are incorporated into the recipe calculations. These nutrients can affect the *PointsPlus* values.
- Alcohol is included in our *PointsPlus* calculations. Because alcohol information is generally not included on nutrition labels, it's not an option to include when using the hand calculator or the online calculator. But since we incorporate alcohol information from our nutritionists you might notice discrepancies between the *PointsPlus* values you see in our recipes, and the values you get using the calculator. *PointsPlus* values listed for our recipes are the most accurate values.

Shopping for Ingredients

As you learn to eat healthier and add more Power Foods to your meals, remember these tips for choosing foods wisely:

- Purchase lean meats and poultry, and trim them of all visible fat before cooking. When poultry is cooked with the skin on, we recommend removing the skin before eating. Nutritional information for recipes that include meat, poultry, and fish is based on cooked, skinless boneless portions (unless otherwise stated), with the fat trimmed.

► Whenever possible, our recipes call for seafood that is sustainable and deemed the most healthful for human consumption so that your choice of seafood is not only good for the oceans but also good for you. For more information about the best seafood choices and to download a pocket guide, go to **environmentaldefensefund.org** or **montereybayaquarium.org**. For information about mercury and seafood go to **weightwatchers.ca**.

► For best flavour, maximum nutrient content, and the lowest prices, buy fresh, local produce, such as vegetables, leafy greens, and fruits in season. Rinse them thoroughly before using and keep a supply of cut-up vegetables and fruits in your refrigerator for convenient, healthy snacks.

► Explore your market for whole-grain products such as whole wheat and whole-grain breads and pastas, brown rice, bulgur, barley, cornmeal, whole wheat couscous, oats, and quinoa to enjoy with your meals.

Preparation and Measuring

► Take a couple of minutes to read through the ingredients and directions before you start to prepare a recipe. This will prevent you from discovering midway through that you don't have an important ingredient or that a recipe requires several hours of marinating. And it's also a good idea to assemble all ingredients and utensils within easy reach before you begin a recipe.

► The success of any recipe depends on accurate weighing and measuring. The effectiveness of the Weight Watchers program and the accuracy of the nutritional analysis depend on correct measuring as well. Use the following techniques:

   ■ Weigh food such as meat, poultry, and fish on a food scale.

   ■ To measure liquids, use a standard glass or plastic measuring cup placed on a level surface. For amounts less than 60 ml (1/4 cup), use standard measuring spoons.

   ■ To measure dry ingredients, use metal or plastic measuring cups that come in 60 ml, 75 ml, 125 ml, and 250 ml (1/4-, 1/3-, 1/2-, and 1-cup) sizes. Fill the appropriate cup and level it with the flat edge of a knife or spatula. For amounts less than 60 ml (1/4 cup), use standard measuring spoons.

French-Style Roast Chicken,
page 88

Contents

Escarole Salad Pizza,
page 154

Recipes by *PointsPlus®* value

PointsPlus value: *1*

Chunky Guacamole, 141

Spicy Garlic and Onion Pita
Chips, 160

Sugar and Spice Popcorn, 161

PointsPlus value: *2*

Chicken Satay with Spicy Peanut
Sauce, 135

Crab Salad–Topped Cucumber, 146

Curried Fruit and Nut Popcorn, 159

Food Processor White Bean and
Tomatillo Dip, 139

Provençal Tomato Tart, 151

Shrimp Cakes with Tarragon
Mayonnaise, 134

PointsPlus value: *3*

Caramelized Onion–Feta Squares, 152

Chicken Egg-Drop Soup, 69

Chocolate-Orange Mousse, 163

Classic Devilled Eggs, 145

French Country-Style Omelette, 20

Green Curry Seafood, 136

Jalapeño Hummus, 143

Korean-Style Barbecue Beef, 131

Nachos Pizzeria Style, 157

Oven-Crisped Cod, 108

Oven-Roasted Eggplant–Bell Pepper
Bruschetta, 153

Overstuffed Western Omelette, 19

Pork and Scallion Roll-Ups, 133

Ricotta, Parmesan, and Sun-Dried
Tomato Dip, 142

Sausage and Cabbage Soup, 70

Shrimp Scampi, 186

Southwestern-Style Shrimp Caesar
Salad, 56

Tandoori-Style Chicken, 179

Tuscan-Style Bean Soup, 72

PointsPlus value: *4*

Beef, Tomato, and Peanut Salad, 198

Black Bean and Mushroom
Quesadillas, 148

Broccoli-Polenta Casserole, 123

Cajun-Seasoned Catfish, 111

Chicken and Rice Salad, 199

Chickpea–Goat Cheese Toasts, 156

Easy Herbed Chicken Tenders, 96

Escarole Salad Pizza, 154

Feta-Stuffed Chicken Breasts, 99

Fish and Sweet Onion Vindaloo, 180

Fisherman's Wharf Seafood Stew, 117

Lamb Shish Kebabs, 176

Mini Banana-Walnut Parfaits, 162

New York Deli–Style Quesadillas, 149

Pepper-Crusted Arctic Char with
Mango, 105

Roasted Garlic–Rubbed Sirloin
Steak, 78

Scrambled Eggs with Peppers and
Onion, 24

Shrimp with Black Bean Sauce, 173

Turkey BLTs, 39

PointsPlus® value: 5

Asian Chicken Salad, 53

Asparagus-Chicken Salad with Lemon Dressing, 51

Beef and Parmesan Bruschetta, 130

Crispiest Oven-Fried Chicken, 92

Grilled Chicken and Asparagus with Capers and Basil, 94

Grilled Nectarines with Raspberry Sorbet and Berries, 164

Hearty Beef-Bulgur Loaf, 79

Lamb, Bacon, and Bean Chili, 86

Middle Eastern–Style Chicken Sandwiches, 38

North African Meatball Stew, 80

Rosemary Chicken with Cherry Tomato Sauce, 93

Szechuan Turkey, 172

Tex Mex–Style Frittata, 25

Turkey and Green Bean Salad with Yogourt-Mint Dressing, 54

Turkey-Vegetable Noodle Bowl, 187

Waffle and Berry Breakfast Parfaits, 35

PointsPlus value: 6

Brown Sugar Porridge, 33

Chinese-Style Barbecued Chicken, 100

Curried Bean-Walnut Burgers, 67

Easy Salmon Cakes with Tartar Sauce, 64

Egg, Tomato, and Avocado Tostadas, 22

Kung Pao Chicken, 171

Lemony Arctic Char with Black Bean Salad, 104

Oven-Roasted Vegetable Burritos, 45

Pork Piccata, 182

Pork with Rice Noodles and Vegetables, 61

Salmon and Vegetable Teriyaki, 189

Shepherd's Pie, 87

Tex-Mex Chef's Salad, 193

Thai Steak Skewers, 197

Tuna with Fennel, Orange, and Olive Salad, 109

Turkey Chili with Black Beans, 196

Turkey, Roasted Pepper, and Ricotta Panini, 43

Turkey Sausages with Warm Potato Salad, 102

Two-Grain Stuffed Peppers, 120

Vegetable Dal, 181

PointsPlus value: 7

Apple-Walnut "Stuffed" Pancakes, 32

Asparagus and Shrimp Stir-Fry, 114

Bean Salad–Topped Pita Wedges, 59

Breakfast Strata, 28

Chicken and Mushroom Pizza, 48

Chunky Fish Chowder, 71

Cod with Puttanesca Sauce, 107

Easy Chimichangas, 194

Ginger Shrimp and Vegetables, 201

Greek Orzo and Beef Casserole, 174

Grilled Tuna Niçoise Salad, 55

Ham, Brown Rice, and Pea Salad, 50

Mushroom and Spinach–Stuffed Trout, 110

Niçoise-Style Tuna Sandwiches, 41

Pork Lo Mein, 169

Risotto with Sausage and Greens, 183

Scallop and Bell Pepper Stir-Fry, 192

Shrimp and Chicken Jambalaya, 112

Two-Grain Pancakes, 30

Vegetable-Cheese Quesadillas, 46

Vegetarian Moussaka, 122

PointsPlus value: 8

Baked Cinnamon-Vanilla French Toast, 29

Broiled Lamb Kebabs with Spinach-Lentil Salad, 85

Grilled Nectarines with Raspberry Sorbet and Berries, page 164

Recipes that work with the Simply Filling technique

1

Breakfast

Overstuffed Western Omelette

Overstuffed Western Omelette

LEVEL Basic

PREP 10 min

COOK 10 min

SERVES 2

▲ **125 ml** (½ cup) diced green bell pepper

▲ **125 ml** (½ cup) diced red bell pepper

▲ **2** scallions, thinly sliced

▲ **125 g** (¼ lb) piece low-sodium fat-free Virginia ham, diced

0.5 ml (⅛ tsp) black pepper

▲ **250 ml** (1 cup) fat-free egg substitute

1. Lightly spray medium nonstick skillet with nonstick spray and set over medium heat. Add green and red bell peppers, scallions, ham, and black pepper; cook, stirring, until vegetables are softened, about 5 minutes.

2. Pour in egg substitute and cook until almost set, about 3 minutes, gently lifting edge of eggs with silicone spatula to allow uncooked portion of egg to run underneath. Fold omelette in half and cook until set, about 2 minutes longer. Cut in half and place one half on each of 2 plates.

PER SERVING (½ OF OMELETTE): 266 grams, 144 Cal, 2 g Total Fat, 1 g Sat Fat, 0 g Trans Fat, 25 mg Chol, 674 mg Sod, 9 g Total Carb, 5 g Total Sugar, 2 g Fib, 22 g Prot, 56 mg Calc.

French Country-Style Omelette

3 PointsPlus® value ™ Per Serving

LEVEL Basic

PREP 5 min

COOK 10 min

SERVES 2

▲ 1   **small zucchini, thinly sliced**

▲ **250 ml (1 cup) thinly sliced white mushrooms**

▲ 1   **tomato, seeded and chopped**

2 ml (½ tsp) dried thyme

0.5 ml (⅛ tsp) salt

0.5 ml (⅛ tsp) black pepper

▲ **250 ml (1 cup) fat-free egg substitute**

15 ml (1 Tbsp) low-fat (1%) milk

60 ml (4 Tbsp) crumbled reduced-fat soft goat cheese

30 ml (2 Tbsp) snipped fresh chives

1. Lightly spray medium nonstick skillet with nonstick spray and set over medium heat. Add zucchini, mushrooms, tomato, thyme, salt, and pepper; cook, stirring, until vegetables are softened, about 3 minutes. Transfer to plate.

2. Beat together egg substitute and milk in 500 ml (2 cup) glass measure.

3. Wipe skillet clean. Spray skillet with nonstick spray and set over medium heat. Pour in half of egg mixture and cook until almost set, about 3 minutes, gently lifting edge of eggs with silicone spatula to allow uncooked portion of egg to run underneath. Spoon half of vegetable mixture over half of omelette. Top with 30 ml (2 Tbsp) of goat cheese and 15 ml (1 Tbsp) of chives. Fold unfilled portion of omelette over filling. Slide omelette onto plate and keep warm. Repeat with remaining egg mixture, vegetable mixture, cheese, and chives to make another omelette.

PER SERVING (1 OMELETTE): 314 grams, 119 Cal, 2 g Total Fat, 1 g Sat Fat, 0 g Trans Fat, 3 mg Chol, 470 mg Sod, 10 g Total Carb, 6 g Total Sugar, 2 g Fib, 16 g Prot, 78 mg Calc.

▲ **HEALTHY EXTRA** Double the amount of mushrooms for an even more delicious omelette.

Vitamin & Mineral Supplements

▶ **Check the label.** Choose a supplement that contains no more than 100 percent of the daily recommendation for vitamins and minerals. And check the expiration date—it should be at least six months from the date of purchase.

▶ **Look for the purity symbol.** If a supplement shows the verification logo of the United States Pharmacopeia (USP), the USP confirms that the product contains the ingredients and the amount of each ingredient listed on the label, is free of harmful contaminants, and was manufactured according to safe and sanitary procedures.

▶ **Take it with a meal.** It's best to swallow a supplement during or after a meal because food boosts your body's ability to absorb key nutrients. If you can't stand swallowing pills, try chewable multivitamins.

Egg, Tomato, and Avocado Tostadas

6 PointsPlus® value™

Per Serving

LEVEL Basic

PREP 15 min

BROIL/COOK 15 min

SERVES 4

4	**15 cm (6 inch) corn tortillas**
▲ 1	**large tomato, chopped**
½	**Hass avocado, pitted, peeled, and diced**
▲ 2	**scallions, thinly sliced**
60 ml	**(¼ cup) chopped fresh cilantro**
15 ml	**(1 Tbsp) lime juice**
5 ml	**(1 tsp) olive oil**
0.5 ml	**(⅛ tsp) black pepper**
▲ 1	**200 g (7 oz) baking potato, cooked, peeled, and diced**
▲ 1	**60 g (2 oz) piece low-sodium fat-free ham, chopped**
▲ 500 ml	**(2 cups fat-free egg substitute**
▲ 60 ml	**(¼ cup) fat-free tomatillo salsa**

1. Preheat broiler.

2. Place tortillas, in one layer, on rack of broiler pan. Broil 10 cm (4 inches) from heat until golden, about 2 minutes per side.

3. Meanwhile, mix together tomato, avocado, scallions, cilantro, lime juice, oil, and pepper in medium bowl.

4. Spray medium nonstick skillet with nonstick spray and set over medium heat. Add potato and ham; cook, stirring occasionally, until lightly browned, about 5 minutes. Transfer to small bowl; keep warm.

5. Wipe skillet clean. Spray with nonstick spray and set over medium heat. Add egg substitute and cook until eggs are set, about 4 minutes, pushing egg mixture toward centre of skillet to form large, soft curds. Divide egg mixture evenly among tortillas, then top evenly with potato mixture, tomato mixture, and salsa.

PER SERVING (1 TOSTADA): 292 grams, 239 Cal, 6 g Total Fat, 1 g Sat Fat, 0 g Trans Fat, 8 mg Chol, 542 mg Sod, 28 g Total Carb, 5 g Total Sugar, 5 g Fib, 19 g Prot, 97 mg Calc.

 FYI **Tostadas** are usually made with fried corn tortillas. Broiling the tortillas keeps the fat way down while making them crispy.

Egg, Tomato, and Avocado Tostadas

Scrambled Eggs with Peppers and Onion

4 PointsPlus® value ™ Per Serving

LEVEL Basic
PREP 10 min
COOK 15 min
SERVES 4

▲ **500 ml (2 cups) fat-free egg substitute**

2 ml (½ tsp) dried oregano

1 ml (¼ tsp) salt

1 ml (¼ tsp) black pepper

10 ml (2 tsp) olive oil

▲ **1 red bell pepper, chopped**

▲ **2 Italian frying peppers, chopped**

▲ **½ small red onion, chopped**

▲ **2 cooked small potatoes, cut into small dice**

1. Whisk together egg substitute, oregano, salt, and black pepper in medium bowl.

2. Heat oil in large nonstick skillet over medium heat. Add bell pepper, frying peppers, and onion; cook, stirring, until softened, about 8 minutes. Stir in potatoes and cook, stirring, until heated through, about 3 minutes. Transfer to plate.

3. Wipe skillet clean. Spray with nonstick spray and set over medium heat. Add egg mixture and cook until eggs begin to set, about 1 ½ minutes, pushing egg mixture toward centre of skillet to form large soft curds. Stir in vegetable mixture and cook until heated through, about 2 minutes longer.

PER SERVING (¼ OF EGGS): 251 grams, 161 Cal, 3 g Total Fat, 0 g Sat Fat, 0 g Trans Fat, 0 mg Chol, 403 mg Sod, 20 g Total Carb, 5 g Total Sugar, 2 g Fib, 14 g Prot, 58 mg Calc.

▲ **HEALTHY EXTRA** Serve a slice of fat-free Swiss cheese alongside each portion of eggs. A 20 g (¾ oz) slice of fat-free cheese with each serving will increase the *PointsPlus* value by *1*.

Tex Mex–Style Frittata

LEVEL Basic

PREP 10 min

COOK 15 min

SERVES 4

▲ **4**   **large eggs**

▲ **4**   **large egg whites**

▲ **60 ml**   **(¼ cup) fat-free milk**

10 ml   **(2 tsp) chili powder**

1 ml   **(¼ tsp) salt**

▲ **250 g** **(1 cup) frozen corn kernels, thawed**

▲ **1**   **125 ml (4 oz) can chopped mild green chiles, drained**

▲ **12**   **cherry tomatoes, halved**

125 g   **(½ cup) shredded, reduced-fat sharp Cheddar cheese**

1. Beat eggs, egg whites, milk, chili powder, and salt in large bowl. Stir in corn and chiles.

2. Spray medium nonstick skillet with nonstick spray and set over medium heat. Add egg mixture; top evenly with tomatoes. Cover and cook until eggs are almost set, about 10 minutes. Sprinkle with Cheddar; cook, covered until eggs are set and cheese is melted, about 5 minutes longer. Cut frittata into 4 wedges. Serve hot, warm, or at room temperature.

PER SERVING (1 WEDGE): 227 grams, 200 Cal, 9 g Total Fat, 4 g Sat Fat, 0 g Trans Fat, 223 mg Chol, 308 mg Sod, 17 g Total Carb, 5 g Total Sugar, 3 g Fib, 17 g Prot, 153 mg Calc.

▲ **HEALTHY EXTRA** Serve toasted slices of reduced-calorie bread alongside each portion of frittata (2 slices of reduced-calorie bread with each serving will increase the *PointsPlus* value by *3*).

On-The-Go Breakfast Burrito

On-The-Go Breakfast Burrito

8 PointsPlus® value
Per Serving

LEVEL Basic

PREP 10 min

COOK 5 min

SERVES 1

5 ml	**(1 tsp) canola oil**
▲ **125 ml**	**(½ cup) fat-free egg substitute**
0.5 ml	**(⅛ tsp) black pepper**
1	**17 cm (7 inch) reduced-fat whole wheat tortilla, warmed**
45 ml	**(3 Tbsp) shredded reduced-fat pepper Jack cheese**
▲ **1**	**small tomato, chopped**
▲ **1**	**large scallion, thinly sliced**
▲ **30 ml**	**(2 Tbsp) fat-free salsa**

1. Heat oil in medium nonstick skillet over medium heat.

2. Whisk together egg substitute and pepper in small bowl until frothy. Pour into skillet and cook, stirring, until just set, about 2 minutes.

3. Spoon eggs onto warm tortilla. Top with pepper Jack, tomato, scallion, and salsa. Roll tortilla up to enclose filling.

PER SERVING (1 BURRITO): 331 grams, 301 Cal, 11 g Total Fat, 3 g Sat Fat, 0 g Trans Fat, 15 mg Chol, 748 mg Sod, 32 g Total Carb, 10 g Total Sugar, 3 g Fib, 22 g Prot, 312 mg Calc.

▲ **HEALTHY EXTRA** This burrito makes a perfect brown-bag breakfast. Wrap it tightly in foil to keep it nice and warm. And be sure to pack along a peeled and sectioned orange for a refreshing finish.

Breakfast Strata

LEVEL Basic

PREP 20 min

COOK/BAKE 1 hr 10 min

SERVES 8

30 ml	**(2 Tbsp) canola oil**
▲ 2	**onions, chopped**
8	**slices turkey bacon, cut into 1.25 cm (½ inch) pieces**
▲ 250 ml	**(1 cup) grape tomatoes, halved**
▲ 500 ml	**(2 cups) fat-free milk**
▲ 3	**large eggs**
▲ 3	**large egg whites**
2 ml	**(½ tsp) dried oregano**
▲ 16	**slices reduced-calorie whole-wheat bread, cut into 1.25 cm (½ inch) cubes**
250 ml	**(1 cup) shredded reduced-fat Swiss cheese**

1. Spray 23 x 33 cm (9 x 13 inch) baking dish with nonstick spray.

2. Heat oil in large nonstick skillet set over medium heat. Add onions and bacon; cook, stirring, until onions are softened and bacon is crisp cooked, about 8 minutes. Remove skillet from heat; stir in tomatoes.

3. Whisk together milk, eggs, egg whites, and oregano in medium bowl. Spread half of bread cubes in prepared baking dish; top with half of onion mixture and half of Swiss. Pour half of milk mixture evenly over cheese. Repeat to make one more layer. Cover baking dish with plastic wrap and refrigerate at least 1 hour or up to overnight.

4. Preheat oven to 180°C (350°F).

5. Remove plastic wrap from strata. Bake until puffed, golden, and knife inserted into centre comes out clean, about 1 hour. Let stand 5 minutes before cutting into 8 portions.

PER SERVING (⅛ OF STRATA): 223 grams, 257 Cal, 10 g Total Fat, 4 g Sat Fat, 0 g Trans Fat, 103 mg Chol, 518 mg Sod, 29 g Total Carb, 8 g Total Sugar, 7 g Fib, 17 g Prot, 286 mg Calc.

FYI A strata is **an ideal company dish**, as it can be prepared way ahead. Refrigerating it overnight gives the bread enough time to absorb all of the great flavours.

Baked Cinnamon-Vanilla French Toast

8 PointsPlus value
Per Serving

LEVEL Basic
PREP 15 min
BAKE 25 min
SERVES 6

500 ml	**(2 cups) low-fat (1%) milk**
▲ **3**	**large eggs**
▲ **2**	**large egg whites**
10 ml	**(2 tsp) sugar**
10 ml	**(2 tsp) vanilla extract**
5 ml	**(1 tsp) ground cinnamon**
1	**500 g (1 pound) loaf challah or other egg bread, cut into 12 slices**
30 ml	**(6 tsp) pure maple syrup**

1. Preheat oven to 220˚C (425°F). Spray two jelly-roll pans with nonstick spray.

2. Whisk together milk, eggs, egg whites, sugar, vanilla, and cinnamon in pie plate or large shallow bowl.

3. Dip bread, one slice at a time, into milk mixture, turning to coat well on each side. Transfer to prepared pans.

4. Bake French toast until slightly puffed and browned, about 12 minutes per side. Serve with maple syrup.

PER SERVING (2 SLICES FRENCH TOAST AND 5 ML [1 TSP] MAPLE SYRUP): 202 grams, 318 Cal, 8 g Total Fat, 3 g Sat Fat, 0 g Trans Fat, 148 mg Chol, 464 mg Sod, 46 g Total Carb, 11 g Total Sugar, 2 g Fib, 14 g Prot, 188 mg Calc.

▲ **HEALTHY EXTRA** Serve this enticing buttery, vanilla-scented French toast with a generous bowl of fresh berries.

Two-Grain Pancakes

LEVEL Basic
PREP 15 min
COOK 20 min
SERVES 4

▲ 1   **large egg**

▲ 1   **large egg white**

▲ **250 ml (1 cup) plain fat-free yogourt**

▲ **125 ml (½ cup) unsweetened applesauce**

15 ml (1 Tbsp) canola oil

15 ml (1 Tbsp) honey

175 ml (¾ cup) white whole wheat flour

125 ml (½ cup) buckwheat flour

10 ml (2 tsp) baking powder

1 ml (¼ tsp) salt

40 ml (8 tsp) pure maple syrup

1. Whisk together egg, egg white, yogourt, applesauce, oil, and honey in small bowl. Whisk together white whole wheat flour, buckwheat flour, baking powder, and salt in large bowl. Add yogourt mixture to flour mixture, stirring just until flour mixture is moistened.

2. Spray large nonstick griddle or skillet with nonstick spray and set over medium heat. Pour 60 ml (¼ cupfuls) of batter onto griddle. Cook until bubbles appear and edges of pancakes look dry, about 3 minutes. Turn pancakes over and cook until golden brown on second side, about 3 minutes longer. Transfer to platter and keep warm. Repeat with remaining batter, making total of 12 pancakes.

PER SERVING (3 PANCAKES AND 10 ML [2 TSP] MAPLE SYRUP): 172 grams, 275 Cal, 6 g Total Fat, 1 g Sat Fat, 0 g Trans Fat, 54 mg Chol, 401 mg Sod, 50 g Total Carb, 20 g Total Sugar, 5 g Fib, 10 g Prot, 132 mg Calc.

▲ **HEALTHY EXTRA** Add a handful of fresh blueberries and strawberries to each serving of pancakes.

Two-Grain Pancakes

Apple-Walnut "Stuffed" Pancakes

LEVEL Basic
PREP 15 min
COOK 20 min
SERVES 6

5 ml	**(1 tsp) butter**
▲ **1**	**large apple, peeled, cored, and chopped**
15 ml	**(3 tsp) sugar**
2 ml	**(½ tsp) ground cinnamon**
0.5 ml	**(⅛ tsp) ground nutmeg**
500 ml	**(2 cups) reduced-fat all-purpose baking mix**
30 ml	**(2 Tbsp) finely chopped walnuts**
310 ml	**(1 ¼ cups) low-fat (1%) milk**
▲ **1**	**large egg, lightly beaten**

1. Melt butter in large nonstick skillet over medium heat. Add apple, 5 ml (1 tsp) of sugar, the cinnamon, and nutmeg. Cook, stirring, until apple is tender, about 4 minutes. Transfer apple mixture to bowl.

2. Stir together baking mix, walnuts, milk, egg, and remaining 10 ml (2 tsp) sugar in large bowl until blended.

3. Spray nonstick griddle or skillet with nonstick spray and set over medium heat. Pour scant 60 ml (¼ cupfuls) of batter onto griddle. Immediately spoon 15 ml (1 Tbsp) of apple mixture onto each pancake. Cook until bubbles appear and edges of pancakes look dry, about 3 minutes. Turn pancakes over and cook until golden brown on second side, about 3 minutes longer. Transfer to platter and keep warm. Repeat with remaining batter, making total of 12 pancakes.

PER SERVING (2 PANCAKES): 143 grams, 237 Cal, 7 g Total Fat, 2 g Sat Fat, 0 g Trans Fat, 39 mg Chol, 501 mg Sod, 39 g Total Carb, 11 g Total Sugar, 1 g Fib, 6 g Prot, 113 mg Calc.

FYI Use a **Golden Delicious apple** if you prefer more sweetness and a **Granny Smith apple** if a tart-sweet flavour is more to your liking.

Brown Sugar Porridge

LEVEL Basic

PREP 15 min

COOK 20 min

SERVES 6

▲ **375 ml** **(1 ½ cups) water**

▲ **250 ml** **(1 cup) whole wheat couscous**

1 ml **(¼ tsp) salt**

750 ml **(3 cups) low-fat (1%) milk**

45 ml **(3 Tbsp) brown sugar**

60 ml **(¼ cup) fat-free egg substitute**

60 ml **(¼ cup) wheat germ**

7 ml **(1 ½ tsp) vanilla extract**

1. Bring water to boil in large, heavy saucepan over high heat. Stir in couscous and salt. Reduce heat and simmer until water is absorbed, about 2 minutes. Remove saucepan from heat and fluff couscous with fork. Cover and let stand 5 minutes.

2. Stir milk and brown sugar into couscous. Bring to boil over medium-high heat, whisking frequently to break up lumps. Reduce heat to medium-low and cook, stirring frequently, until mixture is slightly thickened, about 5 minutes. Remove saucepan from heat.

3. Whisk together 125 ml (½ cup) of couscous mixture and the egg substitute in small bowl. Return mixture to saucepan; cook over low heat, stirring, until porridge is thick and creamy, about 5 minutes longer. Stir in wheat germ and vanilla.

PER SERVING (GENEROUS 175 ML [¾ CUP] PORRIDGE): 241 grams, 242 Cal, 3 g Total Fat, 1 g Sat Fat, 0 g Trans Fat, 5 mg Chol, 185 mg Sod, 45 g Total Carb, 13 g Total Sugar, 5 g Fib, 12 g Prot, 176 mg Calc.

▲ **HEALTHY EXTRA** Top each serving of this good-for-you porridge with sliced strawberries or diced apple.

Living the Good Health Guidelines

Milk, Cheese & Yogourt

▶ **Prepare hot cereal a different way.** Instead of using water, as the package directions suggest, cook hot cereal with fat-free milk. It will give your oatmeal or farina (Cream of Wheat) a creamier than usual texture and will start your day with a healthy serving of calcium.

▶ **Count your coffee.** If you aren't crazy about milk, remember that the milk you put in your coffee counts toward your daily intake. So treat yourself to an afternoon pick-me-up of fat-free café au lait, latte, or cappuccino and know you'll be doing your health a favour along with your taste buds.

▶ **Add cheese and milk to egg dishes.** Cooking up a soufflé, strata, quiche, or frittata can be a delicious way to incorporate a dairy serving into your daily menu, because these dishes typically include milk and cheese. What's more, they are versatile—you can serve one for brunch, lunch, or dinner.

Waffle and Berry Breakfast Parfaits

LEVEL Basic

PREP 15 min

COOK None

SERVES 6

▲ **2** **175 ml (6 oz) containers raspberries**

15 ml **(1 Tbs) granulated sugar**

Grated zest of ½ orange

1 **450 g (15 oz) container fat-free ricotta cheese**

45 ml **(3 Tbsp) confectioners' sugar**

2 ml **(½ tsp) ground cinnamon**

0.5 ml **(⅛ tsp) ground nutmeg**

6 **frozen low-fat waffles, toasted and cut into pieces**

1. Toss together raspberries, granulated sugar, and orange zest in medium bowl. Let stand 5 minutes.

2. Combine ricotta, confectioners' sugar, cinnamon, and nutmeg in food processor and purée. Alternately layer ricotta mixture, waffle pieces, and berry mixture in 6 parfait glasses or goblets, ending with berries.

PER SERVING (1 PARFAIT): 169 grams, 189 Cal, 2 g Total Fat, 2 g Sat Fat, 0 g Trans Fat, 19 mg Chol, 224 mg Sod, 34 g Total Carb, 12 g Total Sugar, 5 g Fib, 9 g Prot, 180 mg Calc.

▲ **HEALTHY EXTRA** Stir 250 ml (1 cup) of diced mango or papaya into the raspberry mixture.

2

Lunch

Middle Eastern–Style Chicken Sandwiches

5 PointsPlus® value

Per Serving

LEVEL Basic

PREP 20 min

COOK None

SERVES 4

▲ 175 ml (¾ cup) plain fat-free yogourt

▲ 125 ml (½ cup) shredded cucumber, squeezed dry

1 small garlic clove, minced

1 ml (¼ tsp) salt

2 17 cm (7 inch) whole wheat pita breads, halved and warmed

▲ 375 ml (1 ½ cups) coarsely shredded skinless cooked chicken breast

▲ 1 large tomato, thinly sliced

▲ ½ small red onion, thinly sliced

▲ 4 small green leaf lettuce leaves

1. To make sauce, stir together yogourt, cucumber, garlic, and salt in small bowl.

2. Spread half of yogourt sauce evenly inside pita halves. Layer chicken, tomato, onion, and lettuce evenly in pita halves. Top evenly with remaining yogourt sauce.

PER SERVING (½ SANDWICH): 201 grams, 207 Cal, 3 g Total Fat, 1 g Sat Fat, 0 g Trans Fat, 46 mg Chol, 385 mg Sod, 25 g Total Carb, 5 g Total Sugar, 3 g Fib, 22 g Prot, 0 g Alcohol, 0 g Sugar Alcohol, 78 mg Calc.

▲ **HEALTHY EXTRA** Serve these sandwiches with a refreshing fruit salad of sliced kiwi, raspberries, and orange sections topped with very thinly sliced fresh mint.

Turkey BLTs

LEVEL Basic

PREP 10 min

COOK 10 min

SERVES 4

30 ml | **(2 Tbsp) fat-free mayonnaise**

Grated zest of ½ lemon

4 | **slices whole wheat bread, toasted**

▲ 4 | **green leaf lettuce leaves**

▲ 250 g | **(8 oz) thinly sliced no-salt added fat-free skinless turkey breast**

▲ 1 | **large tomato, sliced**

4 | **slices turkey bacon, crisp cooked**

1. Stir together mayonnaise and lemon zest in cup.

2. Spread mayonnaise mixture evenly on 2 slices of bread. Layer bread evenly with lettuce, turkey, tomato, and bacon. Cover with remaining 2 slices bread. Cut sandwiches in half.

PER SERVING (½ SANDWICH): 158 grams, 166 Cal, 5 g Total Fat, 1 g Sat Fat, 0 g Trans Fat, 39 mg Chol, 329 mg Sod, 17 g Total Carb, 3 g Total Sugar, 3 g Fib, 16 g Prot, 29 mg Calc.

▲ **HEALTHY EXTRA** Make this classic sandwich even more flavourful by adding thin slices of sweet onion.

Niçoise-Style
Tuna Sandwiches

Niçoise-Style Tuna Sandwiches

LEVEL Basic

PREP 20 min

COOK None

SERVES 4

1	**250 g (8 oz) crusty round bread, split**
30 ml	**(2 Tbsp) red wine vinegar**
10 ml	**(2 tsp) extra-virgin olive oil**
1 ml	**(¼ tsp) black pepper**
▲ 2	**150 g (5 oz) cans low-sodium water-packed chunk light tuna, drained**
▲ 1	**hard-cooked large egg, peeled and chopped**
▲ 2	**scallions, thinly sliced**
8	**pitted Kalamata olives, chopped**
15 ml	**(1 Tbsp) capers, drained and finely chopped**
▲ 2	**tomatoes, thinly sliced**
125 ml	**(½ cup) lightly packed fresh basil leaves**

1. Remove enough bready centre from bread halves to leave 2.5 cm (1 inch) shell. (Reserve bready centre for another use, such as for making fresh bread crumbs.)

2. To make dressing, whisk together vinegar, oil, and pepper in cup. Brush over cut sides of bread.

3. Flake tuna in medium bowl. Stir in egg, scallions, olives, and capers.

4. On bottom of bread, layer half of tomato slices and basil leaves. Spread tuna mixture on top of basil. Arrange remaining tomato slices and basil over tuna. Cover with top of bread. Wrap tightly in foil; refrigerate at least 2 hours. Cut into 4 wedges to serve.

PER SERVING (1 WEDGE): 203 grams, 260 Cal, 8 g Total Fat, 1 g Sat Fat, 0 g Trans Fat, 104 mg Chol, 628 mg Sod, 20 g Total Carb, 4 g Total Sugar, 2 g Fib, 27 g Prot, 49 mg Calc.

 FYI This tasty sandwich is **perfect picnic food**, as it can be prepared early in the day and kept in a cooler for up to 8 hours.

Fruits & Vegetables

▶ **Have fruit with every meal.** At breakfast, top whole-grain cereal with sliced banana or berries. Have an apple or nectarine with lunch. And after dinner, treat yourself to poached pears or spiced fruit compote.

▶ **Challenge your taste buds.** Every week, peruse the produce section at the grocery store and choose a new fruit or vegetable to try—star fruit, Asian pears, rutabaga, beet greens, jicama, or whatever strikes your fancy. It's a fun, easy way to discover new favourites and add them to your healthy-foods repertoire.

▶ **Stash fruits and vegetables in your freezer.** Whether you're tossing together a last-minute fruit salad, making a quick topping for cake or frozen yogourt (with berries, mango, pineapple, and peaches), or stir-frying veggies and meat, it's smart to have frozen produce on hand.

Turkey, Roasted Pepper, and Ricotta Panini

6
PointsPlus
value
Per Serving

LEVEL Basic

PREP 25 min

COOK 5 min

SERVES 2

▲ **125 ml** (½ cup) fat-free ricotta cheese, drained

4 slices whole grain bread

▲ **250 ml** (1 cup) lightly packed baby spinach

▲ **75 ml** (⅓ cup) roasted red peppers (not packed in oil), thickly sliced

4 large fresh basil leaves

▲ **4** 30 g (1 oz) slices no-salt added fat-free skinless turkey breast

1. Spread ricotta evenly over 2 slices of bread. Layer half of spinach, roasted peppers, basil, and turkey over cheese. Cover with remaining 2 slices bread. Gently flatten each sandwich.

2. Lightly spray large heavy skillet with nonstick spray and set over medium heat. Add sandwiches and top with weight such as another pan. Cook until bread is crisp and golden, about 3 minutes. Turn sandwiches over; weight them and cook until second side is crisp and golden, about 3 minutes longer.

PER SERVING (1 SANDWICH): 222 grams, 267 Cal, 4 g Total Fat, 1 g Sat Fat, 0 g Trans Fat, 40 mg Chol, 505 mg Sod, 33 g Total Carb, 6 g Total Sugar, 4 g Fib, 24 g Prot, 161 mg Calc.

FYI For a classic "grilled" effect, cook the **panini** in an electric panini maker or in a stovetop grill pan.

Salmon-Veggie Sandwiches

8 PointsPlus® value

Per Serving

LEVEL Basic

PREP 15 min

COOK None

SERVES 2

▲ 1   **215 g (7 ½ oz) can no salt added salmon, drained and flaked**

45 ml   **(3 Tbsp) fat-free mayonnaise**

▲ 125 ml   **(½ cup) chopped celery**

▲ 125 ml   **(½ cup) finely chopped red onion**

30 ml   **(2 Tbsp) chopped fresh dill**

10 ml   **(2 tsp) Dijon mustard**

    Grated zest and juice of 1 lemon

4   **slices whole wheat bread, toasted**

4   **tomato slices**

▲ 125 ml   **(½ cup) lightly packed baby arugula or spinach**

1. Stir together salmon, mayonnaise, celery, onion, dill, mustard, and lemon zest and juice in medium bowl.

2. Spread salmon mixture evenly over 2 slices of toast. Top each with 2 tomato slices and 60 ml (¼ cup) of arugula. Cover sandwiches with remaining toast slices.

PER SERVING (1 SANDWICH): 315 grams, 306 Cal, 10 g Total Fat, 2 g Sat Fat, 0 g Trans Fat, 23 mg Chol, 704 mg Sod, 39 g Total Carb, 8 g Total Sugar, 7 g Fib, 21 g Prot, 293 mg Calc.

▲ **HEALTHY EXTRA** Add very thin slices of English (seedless) cucumber to the sandwiches.

Oven-Roasted Vegetable Burritos

LEVEL Basic
PREP 25 min
ROAST 40 min
SERVES 4

▲ 1   **500 g (1 lb) eggplant, cut into 2 cm (¾ inch) chunks**

▲ 2   **red bell peppers, cut into 2 cm (¾ inch) pieces**

▲ 1   **zucchini, cut into 2 cm (¾ inch) chunks**

2 ml   **(½ tsp) salt**

4   **20 cm (8 inch) low-fat whole wheat tortillas, warmed**

▲ 250 ml **(1 cup) thinly sliced romaine lettuce**

▲ 1   **large tomato, seeded and chopped**

▲ 1   **jalapeño pepper, seeded and minced**

125 ml **(½ cup) shredded reduced-fat Monterey Jack cheese**

1. Preheat oven to 230°C (450°F).

2. Toss together eggplant, bell peppers, zucchini, and salt in large roasting pan; spray with nonstick spray. Toss again and spread in pan. Roast vegetables, stirring occasionally, until tender and lightly browned, about 40 minutes.

3. Spoon one-fourth of roasted vegetables on each tortilla. Top with one-fourth of lettuce, tomato, jalapeño, and Monterey Jack. Fold two opposite sides of each tortilla over to enclose filling.

PER SERVING (1 BURRITO): 349 grams, 215 Cal, 6 g Total Fat, 2 g Sat Fat, 0 g Trans Fat, 10 mg Chol, 557 mg Sod, 39 g Total Carb, 9 g Total Sugar, 7 g Fib, 9 g Prot, 227 mg Calc.

▲ **HEALTHY EXTRA** If you are feeling super-hungry, spread fat-free refried beans over each tortilla before adding the vegetables (60 ml [¼ cup] of fat-free refried beans with each serving will increase the *PointsPlus* value by *1*).

Vegetable-Cheese Quesadillas

LEVEL Basic

PREP 20 min

BROIL/COOK 25 min

SERVES 4

▲ 2   **small zucchini, thinly sliced**

▲ 2   **red bell peppers, sliced**

2 ml   **(½ tsp) dried oregano**

8   **20 cm (8 inch) fat-free whole wheat tortillas**

120 ml   **(8 Tbsp) shredded reduced-fat Montery Jack cheese**

▲ 3   **scallions, thinly sliced**

▲ 125 ml   **(½ cup) fat-free salsa**

1. Preheat broiler. Line baking sheet with nonstick foil.

2. Spread zucchini and bell peppers on prepared baking sheet. Lightly spray with nonstick spray; sprinkle with oregano. Broil 12.5 cm (5 inches) from heat, stirring once or twice, until vegetables are softened and lightly charred, about 12 minutes.

3. Place 4 tortillas on work surface. Top each with 15 ml (1 Tbsp) of Monterey Jack, one-fourth of vegetable mixture, one-fourth of scallions, and 15 ml (1 Tbsp) of cheese. Cover with remaining 4 tortillas, lightly pressing down.

4. Spray large nonstick skillet with nonstick spray and set over medium heat. Add 1 quesadilla and cook until crisp and cheese begins to melt, about 1½ minutes per side. Transfer to cutting board; keep warm. Cook remaining 3 quesadillas. Cut each into 4 wedges. Serve with salsa.

PER SERVING (4 WEDGES AND 30 ML [2 TBSP] SALSA): 242 grams, 234 Cal, 4 g Total Fat, 2 g Sat Fat, 0 g Trans Fat, 10 mg Chol, 657 mg Sod, 51 g Total Carb, 7 g Total Sugar, 6 g Fib, 12 g Prot, 164 mg Calc.

Vegetable-Cheese
Quesadillas

Chicken and Mushroom Pizza

LEVEL Basic
PREP 25 min
BAKE/COOK 25 min
SERVES 6

45 ml	(3 Tbsp) grated Parmesan cheese
15 ml	(1 Tbsp) fat-free mayonnaise
▲ 10 ml	(2 tsp) fat-free milk
2 ml	(½ tsp) dried thyme
▲ 250 g	(½ lb) skinless boneless chicken breasts, cut crosswise into 1.25 cm (½ inch) slices
125 ml	(½ cup) cornflake crumbs
▲ 500 ml	(2 cups) thinly sliced white or cremini mushrooms
1 ml	(¼ tsp) black pepper
▲ 175 ml	(¾ cup) fat-free ricotta cheese
1	290 g (10 oz) prebaked thin whole wheat pizza crust
125 ml	(½ cup) shredded part-skim mozzarella cheese

1. Preheat oven to 230°C (450°F). Spray small baking dish with nonstick spray.

2. Stir together Parmesan, mayonnaise, milk, and thyme in medium bowl. Add chicken and toss to coat evenly.

3. Put cornflake crumbs in large zip-close plastic bag. Add chicken and shake bag until coated. Place chicken in prepared baking dish in single layer. Bake until golden brown and cooked through, about 5 minutes per side.

4. Meanwhile, spray large nonstick skillet with olive oil nonstick spray and set over medium-high heat. Add mushrooms and sprinkle with pepper; cook, stirring, until mushrooms release their juice and it is evaporated.

5. Spread ricotta over pizza crust. Top with mushrooms, chicken, and mozzarella. Bake until cheese is melted, about 15 minutes. Cut into 6 wedges

PER SERVING (1 WEDGE): 150 grams, 263 Cal, 6 g Total Fat, 3 g Sat Fat, 0 g Trans Fat, 33 mg Chol, 454 mg Sod, 33 g Total Carb, 4 g Total Sugar, 5 g Fib, 20 g Prot, 211 mg Calc.

▲ **HEALTHY EXTRA** Cook 1 zucchini and 1 red bell pepper, thinly sliced, along with the mushrooms in step 4.

Potato-Cheese Pita Pizzas

8 PointsPlus value ™

Per Serving

LEVEL Basic

PREP 25 min

BAKE 10 min

SERVES 4

▲ **500 ml (2 cups) thinly sliced cooked potatoes**

10 ml (2 tsp) chopped fresh rosemary

1 ml (¼ tsp black pepper

125 ml (½ cup) shredded fontina cheese

▲ **125 ml (½ cup) shredded fat-free mozzarella cheese**

4 17 cm (7 inch) whole wheat pita breads

1. Preheat oven to 230°C (450°F). Spray baking sheet with nonstick spray.

2. Toss together potatoes, rosemary, and pepper in medium bowl. Sprinkle fontina and mozzarella evenly over pita breads.

3. Divide potato mixture evenly among pitas; lightly spray with nonstick spray. Place pizzas on prepared baking sheet. Bake until potatoes are heated through and cheese is melted, about 8 minutes.

PER SERVING (1 PIZZA): 170 grams, 313 Cal, 6 g Total Fat, 3 g Sat Fat, 0 g Trans Fat, 18 mg Chol, 623 mg Sod, 52 g Total Carb, 2 g Total Sugar, 7 g Fib, 16 g Prot, 217 mg Calc.

Ham, Brown Rice, and Pea Salad

7 PointsPlus value
Per Serving

LEVEL Basic
PREP 25 min
COOK 25 min
SERVES 6

▲ **250 ml (1 cup) brown rice**

▲ **500 ml (2 cups) frozen baby peas**

▲ **1**   **250 g (½ lb) piece low-sodium fat-free ham, cut into 1.25 cm (½ inch)**

▲ **500 ml (2 cups) cherry tomatoes, halved**

125 ml (½ cup) shredded Gruyère cheese

▲ **2**   **scallions, thinly sliced**

30 ml (2 Tbsp) chopped fresh mint

45 ml (3 Tbsp) champagne vinegar or cider vinegar

10 ml (2 tsp) olive oil

1 ml (¼ tsp) black pepper

1. Cook rice according to package directions, omitting salt if desired and adding peas during last 5 minutes of cooking time. Drain rice with peas in colander; let cool.

2. Transfer rice mixture to serving bowl. Add remaining ingredients; toss to coat evenly.

PER SERVING (ABOUT 375 ML [1 ½ CUPS]):
260 grams, 277 Cal, 8 g Total Fat, 3 g Sat Fat, 0 g Trans Fat, 31 mg Chol, 519 mg Sod, 34 g Total Carb, 3 g Total Sugar, 5 g Fib, 16 g Prot, 125 mg Calc.

▲ **HEALTHY EXTRA** Spoon this salad over Boston or Bibb lettuce leaves and serve with whole radishes with their leaves attached.

Asparagus-Chicken Salad with Lemon Dressing

5 PointsPlus value
Per Serving

LEVEL Basic

PREP 15 min

COOK 5 min

SERVES 6

▲ 1   **500 g (1 lb) bunch asparagus, trimmed and cut into 2.5 cm (1 inch) pieces**

Grated zest and juice of 1 lemon

30 ml   **(2 Tbsp) olive oil**

1   **large garlic clove, minced**

2 ml   **(½ tsp) salt**

1 ml   **(¼ tsp) black pepper**

▲ 375 g   **(¾ lb) cooked skinless boneless chicken breast, diced**

▲ 475 ml   **(15 ½ fl oz) can pinto beans, rinsed and drained**

▲ 1   **red bell pepper, chopped**

▲ 250 ml   **(1 cup) grape tomatoes**

▲ 3   **scallions, sliced**

60 ml   **(¼ cup) coarsely chopped fresh basil**

1. Put asparagus in steamer basket; set in large saucepan over 2.5 cm (1 inch) of boiling water. Cook, covered, just until tender, about 4 minutes. Drain in colander; rinse under cold running water. Drain again.

2. To make dressing, whisk together lemon zest and juice, oil, garlic, salt, and black pepper in serving bowl. Add asparagus and remaining ingredients; toss until mixed well.

PER SERVING (GENEROUS 250 ML [1 CUP]):
301 grams, 242 Cal, 3 g Total Fat, 1 g Sat Fat, 0 g Trans Fat, 72 mg Chol, 488 mg Sod, 19 g Total Carb, 4 g Total Sugar, 6 g Fib, 32 g Prot, 66 mg Calc.

▲ **HEALTHY EXTRA** Steam 250 ml (1 cup) of halved snow peas along with the asparagus, and add to the salad in step 2.

Asian Chicken Salad

Asian Chicken Salad

5 PointsPlus value
TM
Per Serving

LEVEL Basic

PREP 20 min

COOK 10 min

SERVES 4

▲ **4**   **150 g (5 oz) skinless boneless chicken breasts**

2 ml   **(½ tsp) salt**

1 ml   **(¼ tsp) black pepper**

2 ml   **(½ tsp) canola oil**

30 ml   **(2 Tbsp) seasoned rice vinegar**

15 ml   **(1 Tbsp) reduced-sodium soy sauce**

15 ml   **(1 Tbsp) Asian (dark) sesame oil**

10 ml   **(2 tsp) grated peeled fresh ginger**

▲ **750 ml**   **(3 cups) coleslaw mix**

▲ **250 ml**   **(1 cup) matchstick-cut carrots**

▲ **1**   **small red bell pepper, thinly sliced**

▲ **4**   **scallions, thinly sliced**

1. Sprinkle chicken with salt and pepper. Heat oil in large nonstick skillet over medium-high heat. Add chicken and cook until browned and cooked through, about 4 minutes per side. Transfer to plate. When cool enough to handle, thinly slice chicken on diagonal.

2. To make dressing, whisk together vinegar, soy sauce, sesame oil, and ginger in serving bowl. Add remaining ingredients; toss to coat evenly. Serve salad topped with chicken breast.

PER SERVING 310 ML [1 ¼ CUPS]: 215 grams, 231 Cal, 7 g Total Fat, 2 g Sat Fat, 0 g Trans Fat, 78 mg Chol, 684 mg Sod, 10 g Total Carb, 6 g Total Sugar, 3 g Fib, 30 g Prot, 54 mg Calc.

▲ **HEALTHY EXTRA** Add a thinly sliced yellow or green bell pepper to the salad for more crunch.

Turkey and Green Bean Salad with Yogourt-Mint Dressing

5 PointsPlus value

Per Serving

LEVEL Basic

PREP 20 min

COOK 5 min

SERVES 4

▲ **500 g** **(1 lb) green beans, trimmed and cut into 2.5 cm (1 inch) pieces**

▲ **1** **500 g (1 lb) piece no-salt added skinless roasted turkey breast, cut into bite-size pieces**

▲ **75 ml** **(⅓ cup) plain fat-free yogourt**

60 ml **(¼ cup) chopped fresh parsley**

30 ml **(2 Tbsp) chopped fresh mint**

Grated zest and juice of 1 lemon

1 ml **(¼ tsp) salt**

1 ml **(1/4 tsp) black pepper**

▲ **4** **large butter or Boston lettuce leaves**

▲ **1** **220 ml (7 fl oz) jar roasted red peppers (not packed in oil), drained and diced**

1. Put green beans in steamer basket; set in large saucepan over 2.5 cm (1 inch) of boiling water. Cook, covered, until tender, about 4 minutes. Drain in colander; rinse under cold running water. Drain again.

2. To make dressing, whisk together yogourt, parsley, mint, lemon zest and juice, salt, and black pepper in small bowl.

3. Arrange lettuce leaves on platter. Place turkey, green beans, and roasted peppers on top of lettuce. Spoon dressing over all.

PER SERVING (¼ OF SALAD): 315 grams, 206 Cal, 5 g Total Fat, 1 g Sat Fat, 0 g Trans Fat, 60 mg Chol, 354 mg Sod, 14 g Total Carb, 5 g Total Sugar, 5 g Fib, 30 g Prot, 101 mg Calc.

FYI You can substitute other dark green vegetables for the green beans, including small **broccoli florets, sugar snap peas, snow peas, or sliced zucchini.**

Grilled Tuna Niçoise Salad

7
PointsPlus©
value
Per Serving

LEVEL Basic

PREP 25 min

COOK/GRILL 15 min

SERVES 6

▲ **500 g**	**(1 lb) small red potatoes, scrubbed**
▲ **250 g**	**(½ lb) haricots verts (slender green beans), trimmed**
▲ **4**	**150 g (5 oz) tuna steaks, 2 cm (¾ inch) thick**
1 ml	**(¼ tsp) salt**
30 ml	**(2 Tbsp) red wine vinegar**
▲ **30 ml**	**(2 Tbsp) reduced-sodium chicken broth**
15 ml	**(1 Tbsp) olive oil**
1	**garlic clove, minced**
1 ml	**(¼ tsp) black pepper**
▲ **1**	**head Boston lettuce, leaves separated**
▲ **2**	**tomatoes, cut into wedges**
12	**niçoise olives**
▲ **2**	**hard-cooked large eggs, peeled and sliced**
15 ml	**(1 Tbsp) nonpareil (tiny) capers, drained**

1. Spray grill rack with nonstick spray. Preheat grill to medium-high or prepare medium-high fire using direct method.

2. Meanwhile, put potatoes in large saucepan and add enough water to cover; bring to boil. Reduce heat and cook until tender, about 12 minutes, adding green beans during last 5 minutes of cooking time. Drain vegetables in colander and rinse under cold running water. Drain again.

3. Sprinkle tuna with salt. Place on grill rack and grill until fish is well marked but still pink in centre, about 2 minutes per side for medium-rare. Transfer tuna to cutting board; let stand 5 minutes. Cut into 0.5 cm (¼ inch) slices.

4. To make dressing, whisk together vinegar, broth, oil, garlic, and pepper in small bowl. Arrange lettuce leaves on platter. Place tuna in centre of platter. Arrange piles of potatoes, green beans, tomatoes, olives, and eggs around tuna. Drizzle dressing over all and sprinkle with capers.

PER SERVING (⅙ OF SALAD): 307 grams, 273 Cal, 7 g Total Fat, 1 g Sat Fat, 0 g Trans Fat, 115 mg Chol, 370 mg Sod, 23 g Total Carb, 4 g Total Sugar, 3 g Fib, 28 g Prot, 61 mg Calc.

FYI Niçoise salad is usually made with canned tuna. Using **grilled tuna** takes this ever-popular salad to a new level.

Southwestern-Style Shrimp Caesar Salad

3 PointsPlus© value
Per Serving

LEVEL Basic

PREP 25 min

COOK None

SERVES 6

60 ml	(¼ cup) fat-free mayonnaise
60 ml	(¼ cup) grated Parmesan cheese
15 ml	(1 Tbsp) lime juice
1	small garlic clove, minced
1 ml	(¼ tsp) black pepper
▲ 1	large head romaine lettuce, torn into pieces
60 ml	(¼ cup) coarsely chopped fresh cilantro
▲ 1	125 ml (4 oz) can chopped mild green chiles, drained
250 ml	(1 cup) fat-free croutons
▲ 500 g	(1 lb) cooked large peeled and deveined shrimp

1. To make dressing, whisk together mayonnaise, Parmesan, lime juice, garlic, and pepper in small bowl.

2. Combine romaine, cilantro, chiles, and croutons in serving bowl. Pour dressing over and toss to coat evenly. Top with shrimp.

PER SERVING (ABOUT 625 ML [2 ½ CUPS]):
192 grams, 152 Cal, 2 g Total Fat, 1 g Sat Fat, 0 g Trans Fat, 151 mg Chol, 517 mg Sod, 11 g Total Carb, 1 g Total Sugar, 2 g Fib, 20 g Prot, 130 mg Calc.

FYI For a more **elegant presentation**, use hearts of romaine lettuce instead of the torn pieces.

**Southwestern-Style
Shrimp Caesar Salad**

Classic Macaroni Salad

LEVEL Basic

PREP 25 min

COOK 15 min

SERVES 4

▲ **250 g** **(8 oz) whole wheat elbow macaroni**

▲ **250 ml** **(1 cup) small broccoli florets**

▲ **1** **large tomato, chopped**

▲ **2** **celery stalks, thinly sliced**

▲ **1** **small red bell pepper, chopped**

▲ **2** **scallions, thinly sliced**

60 ml **(¼ cup) reduced-fat mayonnaise**

▲ **60 ml** **(¼ cup) fat-free sour cream**

15 ml **(1 Tbsp) lemon juice**

2 ml **(½ tsp) dried basil**

2 ml **(½ tsp) salt**

2 ml **(½ tsp) black pepper**

1. Cook macaroni according to package directions, omitting salt if desired. Drain in colander; rinse under cold running water. Drain again. Transfer to serving bowl.

2. Add broccoli, tomato, celery, bell pepper, and scallions to macaroni.

3. To make dressing, whisk together remaining ingredients in small bowl. Drizzle over macaroni mixture and toss to coat evenly.

PER SERVING (GENEROUS 250 ML [1 CUP]):
207 grams, 286 Cal, 6 g Total Fat, 1 g Sat Fat, 0 g Trans Fat, 5 mg Chol, 470 mg Sod, 52 g Total Carb, 6 g Total Sugar, 7 g Fib, 10 g Prot, 76 mg Calc.

Bean Salad–Topped Pita Wedges

PointsPlus value
7
Per Serving

LEVEL Basic
PREP 20 min
BROIL 5 min
SERVES 4

⚠ **475 ml** **(15 ½ fl oz) can no salt added small white beans, rinsed and drained**

⚠ **1** **small red bell pepper, chopped**

⚠ **2** **scallions, chopped**

Grated zest and juice of 1 lemon

Pinch red pepper flakes

4 **17 cm (7 inch) whole wheat pita breads, each cut into 4 wedges**

⚠ **16** **cherry tomatoes, halved**

125 g **(4 oz) reduced-fat soft goat cheese, crumbled**

1. Mix together beans, bell pepper, scallions, lemon zest and juice, and pepper flakes in medium bowl.

2. Preheat broiler.

3. Place pita wedges on baking sheet in single layer. Lightly spray with nonstick spray. Broil 12.5 cm (5 inches) from heat until crisp, about 5 minutes.

4. Spoon bean salad evenly on pita wedges. Top each with 2 tomato halves and sprinkle evenly with goat cheese.

PER SERVING (4 SALAD-TOPPED PITA WEDGES):
237 grams, 289 Cal, 5 g Total Fat, 2 g Sat Fat, 0 g Trans Fat, 5 mg Chol, 481 mg Sod, 52 g Total Carb, 3 g Total Sugar, 10 g Fib, 13 g Prot, 67 mg Calc.

Pork with Rice Noodles and Vegetables

Pork with Rice Noodles and Vegetables

6 PointsPlus® value™ Per Serving

LEVEL Basic
PREP 15 min
COOK 15 min
SERVES 4

100 g	(3 ½ oz) rice stick noodles (½ of 200 g [7 oz] package)
▲ 125 ml	(½ cup) reduced-sodium chicken broth
30 ml	(2 Tbsp) cornstarch
30 ml	(2 Tbsp) reduced-sodium soy sauce
30 ml	(2 Tbsp) brown sugar
30 ml	(2 Tbsp) canola oil
▲ 250 g	(½ lb) lean pork tenderloin, trimmed, sliced, and cut into thin strips
2	large garlic cloves, minced
▲ 170 g	(6 oz) white mushrooms, sliced
▲ 500 ml	(2 cups) broccoli slaw mix
▲ 250 ml	(1 cup) matchstick-cut carrots

1. Plunge noodles into large bowl of hot water; let stand until softened, about 10 minutes; drain.

2. Meanwhile, to make sauce, whisk together broth, cornstarch, soy sauce, and brown sugar in small bowl until smooth.

3. Heat nonstick wok or deep large skillet over high heat until drop of water sizzles in pan; add 5 ml (1 tsp) of oil and swirl to coat pan. Add pork and stir-fry until browned, about 5 minutes. Add garlic and stir-fry until fragrant, about 30 seconds; transfer to medium bowl.

4. Heat remaining 5 ml (1 tsp) oil in wok. Add mushrooms, broccoli slaw, and carrots. Stir-fry until carrots are crisp-tender, about 6 minutes. Re-stir cornstarch mixture; add to wok along with pork. Stir-fry until sauce bubbles and thickens, about 2 minutes. Stir in noodles and stir-fry until heated through, about 2 minutes longer.

PER SERVING (ABOUT 375 ML [1 ½ CUPS]):
201 grams, 237 Cal, 5 g Total Fat, 1 g Sat Fat, 0 g Trans Fat, 32 mg Chol, 466 mg Sod, 33 g Total Carb, 5 g Total Sugar, 2 g Fib, 15 g Prot, 29 mg Calc.

FYI Rice stick noodles, also known as rice vermicelli or rice sticks, are made from rice flour. They only need a brief soak in very hot water to soften enough to eat. Rice sticks come in several different widths, from very thin to wide.

Activity

▶ **Make workout dates.** Instead of meeting a friend for a meal or a drink, head to the gym together. Take an exercise class together. Or take a hike or bike ride. You'll catch up with each other's news while moving your bodies—a healthy way of multitasking.

▶ **Move to energize yourself.** When you're feeling tired or down and you're not truly hungry, instead of automatically reaching for a snack, take a brisk walk in the sun or dance to your favourite tunes. Both forms of movement are likely to boost your mood and your energy level—and neither requires you to consume calories.

▶ **Fit it in.** Contrary to what you may have heard, there's no ideal time of day to exercise. The best time is the one that suits your personality and your schedule. Whenever possible, put exercising on your calendar as if it were a business or doctor's appointment so that you'll be more likely to treat it as a must-do.

Stovetop-Grilled Salmon with Mexican Corn Salad

8 PointsPlus value™ Per Serving

LEVEL Basic

PREP 15 min

ROAST/COOK 30 min

SERVES 4

▲ 2   **290 g (10 oz) packages frozen corn kernels, thawed and patted dry**

▲ 1   **orange or green bell pepper, chopped**

▲ ½   **small red onion, thinly sliced**

125 ml   **(½ cup) chopped fresh cilantro**

▲ 1   **jalapeño pepper, seeded and minced**

45 ml   **(3 Tbsp) lime juice**

15 ml   **(1 Tbsp) honey**

5 ml   **(1 tsp) canola oil**

3 ml   **(¾ tsp) salt**

4   **125 g (¼ lb) salmon fillets**

1. Preheat oven to 230°C (425°F). Spray jelly-roll pan with nonstick spray.

2. Spread corn in prepared pan. Roast, stirring occasionally, until lightly browned, about 20 minutes; let cool completely.

3. Mix together corn, bell pepper, onion, cilantro, jalapeño, lime juice, honey, oil, and 1 ml (¼ tsp) of salt in serving bowl.

4. Heat nonstick ridged grill pan over medium-high heat. Spray salmon fillets with olive oil nonstick spray; sprinkle with remaining 2 ml (½ tsp) salt. Place salmon in grill pan and cook until just opaque in centre, about 4 minutes per side. Serve with corn salad.

PER SERVING (1 SALMON FILLET AND 250 ML [1 CUP] SALAD): 284 grams, 291 Cal, 6 g Total Fat, 1 g Sat Fat, 0 g Trans Fat, 57 mg Chol, 515 mg Sod, 37 g Total Carb, 8 g Total Sugar, 4 g Fib, 26 g Prot, 27 mg Calc.

FYI When **fresh corn** is in season, use it instead of the frozen. Look for ears with moist silk, which ensures the corn has been freshly picked. For this recipe you will need about 6 medium ears of corn to yield 750 ml (3 cups) of kernels.

Easy Salmon Cakes with Tartar Sauce

6 PointsPlus® value™ Per Serving

LEVEL Basic

PREP 30 min

COOK 10 min

SERVES 4

75 ml	**(⅓ cup) + 45 ml (3 Tbsp) fat-free mayonnaise**
15 ml	**(1 Tbsp) capers, drained and chopped**
5 ml	**(1 tsp) lemon juice**
▲ **440 g**	**(14 ¾ oz) can salmon, drained**
1	**scallion, chopped**
▲ **1**	**celery stalk, finely chopped**
60 ml	**(¼ cup) + 45 ml (3 Tbsp) plain dried bread crumbs**
	Few drops hot pepper sauce
10 ml	**(2 tsp) canola oil**

1. To make sauce, stir together 5 ml (⅓ cup) of mayonnaise, the capers, and lemon juice in serving bowl. Cover and refrigerate until ready to serve.

2. To make salmon cakes, with fork, mash salmon with bones in large bowl. Stir in remaining 45 ml (3 Tbsp) mayonnaise, the scallion, celery, 45 ml (3 Tbsp) of bread crumbs, and the hot sauce. Shape into 4 (1.25 cm [½ inch] thick) patties. Cover and refrigerate until firm, about 1 hour.

3. Put remaining 60 ml (¼ cup) bread crumbs on sheet of wax paper. Coat patties with crumbs.

4. Heat oil in large nonstick skillet over medium heat. Add patties and cook until crisp and heated through, about 5 minutes per side. Serve with tartar sauce.

PER SERVING (1 SALMON CAKE AND ABOUT 15 ML [1 TBSP] TARTAR SAUCE): 153 grams, 218 Cal, 11 g Total Fat, 2 g Sat Fat, 0 g Trans Fat, 57 mg Chol, 785 mg Sod, 14 g Total Carb, 3 g Total Sugar, 2 g Fib, 18 g Prot, 163 mg Calc.

FYI There's no need to buy packaged **bread crumbs** as you can easily make your own. Here's how: Tear leftover bread into small pieces and spread in a jelly-roll pan. Let stand until completely hard and dry, which will take about 1 day. (Or dry the bread in a 120°C [250°F] oven for about 30 minutes.) Process the bread pieces in a food processor, in batches if needed, until crumbs form. The crumbs can be stored in the freezer in an airtight container or zip-close plastic freezer bag for up to 2 months.

Easy Salmon Cakes with Tartar Sauce

Mixed Grain and Cheddar Fritters

LEVEL Basic

PREP 15 min

COOK 1 hr 10 min

SERVES 4

▲ **500 ml (2 cups) reduced-sodium vegetable broth**

▲ **125 ml (½ cup) brown rice**

▲ **125 ml (½ cup) quinoa, rinsed and drained**

10 ml (2 tsp) olive oil

▲ **1 onion, finely chopped**

▲ **2 carrots, shredded**

▲ **125 ml (½ cup) fat-free egg substitute**

125 ml (½ cup) shredded reduced-fat Cheddar cheese

45 ml (3 Tbsp) all-purpose flour

2 ml (½ tsp) dried thyme

2 ml (½ tsp) salt

1 ml (¼ tsp) black pepper

1. Bring broth to boil in medium saucepan; stir in rice. Reduce heat and cook, covered, 20 minutes. Stir in quinoa and cook, covered, until rice and quinoa are tender, about 20 minutes longer. Drain off any remaining liquid. Spread rice mixture on large plate and let cool.

2. Heat 5 ml (1 tsp) of oil in medium nonstick skillet over medium heat. Add onion and cook, stirring, until softened, about 5 minutes.

3. Mix together onion and all remaining ingredients except remaining oil in large bowl; stir in rice mixture.

4. Heat remaining 5 ml (1 tsp) oil on nonstick griddle or in large nonstick skillet over medium-high heat. Drop batter, in batches if needed, by 60 ml (¼ cup) amounts onto griddle. Cook until golden, about 3 minutes per side. Repeat with remaining batter, making total of 16 fritters.

PER SERVING (4 FRITTERS): 335 grams, 308 Cal, 8 g Total Fat, 3 g Sat Fat, 0 g Trans Fat, 10 mg Chol, 584 mg Sod, 48 g Total Carb, 7 g Total Sugar, 5 g Fib, 13 g Prot, 162 mg Calc.

▲ **HEALTHY EXTRA** Turn these good-for-you fritters into a satisfying meal by serving them with a lettuce, tomato, and red onion salad dressed with lime juice and a pinch of salt.

Curried Bean-Walnut Burgers

6 PointsPlus® value ™ Per Serving

LEVEL Basic
PREP 25 min
COOK 10 min
SERVES 4

10 ml	**(2 tsp) olive oil**
▲ 1	**onion, finely chopped**
▲ 250 ml	**(1 cup) finely chopped celery**
10 ml	**(2 tsp) curry powder**
1 ml	**(¼ tsp) salt**
1 ml	**(1/4 tsp) hot pepper sauce or to taste**
▲ 1	**475 ml (15 ½ fl oz) can red kidney beans, rinsed, drained, and mashed**
500 ml	**(2 cups) fresh whole wheat bread crumbs (about 4 slices bread)**
▲ 1	**large egg**
60 ml	**(¼ cup) finely chopped walnuts**
▲ 4	**Boston (butter) lettuce leaves**
▲ 4	**thick tomato slices**

1. Heat 5 ml (1 tsp) of oil in medium nonstick skillet over medium heat. Add onion and celery; cook, stirring, until softened, about 5 minutes. Stir in curry powder, salt, and pepper sauce.

2. Mix together onion mixture, beans, bread crumbs, egg, and walnuts in large bowl. Shape mixture into 4 (1.25 cm (½ inch) patties and place on wax paper–lined plate. Refrigerate until firm, at least 30 minutes or up to 4 hours.

3. Heat remaining 5 ml (1 tsp) oil in large nonstick skillet over medium heat. Add patties and cook until golden and heated through, about 4 minutes per side.

4. Place 1 burger on each of 4 plates and place 1 lettuce leaf and 1 tomato slice alongside.

PER SERVING (1 BURGER, 1 LETTUCE LEAF, AND 1 TOMATO SLICE): 212 grams, 248 Cal, 10 g Total Fat, 2 g Sat Fat, 0 g Trans Fat, 53 mg Chol, 443 mg Sod, 32 g Total Carb, 6 g Total Sugar, 8 g Fib, 11 g Prot, 105 mg Calc.

▲ **HEALTHY EXTRA** After turning the burgers over, top each with a slice of fat-free Cheddar cheese. One 20 g (¾ oz) slice of fat-free Cheddar cheese per serving will increase the *PointsPlus* value by *1.*

Chicken Egg-Drop Soup

Chicken Egg-Drop Soup

3 PointsPlus® value ™ Per Serving

LEVEL Basic
PREP 10 min
COOK 20 min
SERVES 6

▲ 1 L (32 fl oz) carton reduced-sodium chicken broth

3 garlic cloves, halved

75 ml (⅓ cup) cornstarch

125 ml (½ cup) water

15 ml (1 Tbsp) reduced-sodium soy sauce

▲ 2 large eggs, lightly beaten

▲ 500 ml (2 cups) lightly packed tender watercress sprigs

▲ 250 ml (1 cup) diced skinless cooked chicken breast

▲ 2 scallions, thinly sliced

1. Combine broth and garlic in large saucepan and bring to boil. Reduce heat and simmer, covered, until flavours are blended, about 12 minutes. Discard garlic.

2. Meanwhile, stir together cornstarch and water in small bowl until smooth. Whisk cornstarch mixture into broth mixture. Cook, stirring constantly, until soup bubbles and thickens, about 3 minutes. Stir in soy sauce.

3. Reduce heat to low. Slowly pour in beaten eggs, while slowly stirring constantly in one direction so strands form. Stir in watercress, chicken, and scallions; cook until watercress is wilted and soup is heated through, about 2 minutes longer.

PER SERVING (250 ML [1 CUP]): 238 grams, 107 Cal, 3 g Total Fat, 1 g Sat Fat, 0 g Trans Fat, 91 mg Chol, 545 mg Sod, 8 g Total Carb, 1 g Total Sugar, 0 g Fib, 12 g Prot, 32 mg Calc.

▲ **HEALTHY EXTRA** Stir 1 large tomato, seeded and diced into the soup along with the watercress in step 3.

Sausage and Cabbage Soup

3 PointsPlus® value

Per Serving

LEVEL Basic

PREP 15 min

COOK 50 min

SERVES 6

10 ml	**(2 tsp) olive oil**
▲ 1	**onion, chopped**
▲ 1	**carrot, diced**
▲ 2	**celery stalks, diced**
1	**170 g (6 oz) piece low-fat kielbasa, thinly sliced**
3	**garlic cloves, minced**
2 L	**(8 cups) water**
3 ml	**(¾ tsp) salt**
2 ml	**(½ tsp) dried thyme**
1 ml	**(¼ tsp) black pepper**
▲ 1	**small head green cabbage, shredded (about 2 L [8 cups])**
▲ 1	**all-purpose potato, peeled and shredded**

1. Heat oil in large saucepan over medium heat. Add onion, carrot, and celery; cook, stirring, until onion is softened, about 5 minutes. Add kielbasa and garlic; cook, stirring, until garlic is fragrant, about 30 seconds. Add water, salt, thyme, and pepper; bring to boil. Reduce heat and simmer, partially covered, 15 minutes.

2. Stir cabbage and potato into soup; return to boil. Reduce heat and simmer, partially covered, until vegetables are tender, about 30 minutes longer.

PER SERVING (GENEROUS 250 ML [1 CUP]):
521 grams, 113 Cal, 3 g Total Fat, 1 g Sat Fat, 0 g Trans Fat, 10 mg Chol, 580 mg Sod, 18 g Total Carb, 7 g Total Sugar, 4 g Fib, 6 g Prot, 82 mg Calc.

▲ **HEALTHY EXTRA** Make this soup even heartier by stirring in a 475 ml (15 ½ fl oz) can of rinsed and drained white beans 10 minutes before the cooking time is up. This will increase the per-serving *PointsPlus* value by *2*.

Chunky Fish Chowder

7 PointsPlus® value ™ Per Serving

LEVEL Basic
PREP 15 min
COOK 20 min
SERVES 4

10 ml	**(2 tsp) olive oil**
▲ 1	**onion, chopped**
▲ 2	**celery stalks, diced**
▲ 500 g	**(1 lb) all-purpose potatoes, peeled and diced**
▲ 500 ml	**(2 cups) no-salt added chicken broth**
1	**175 ml (6 fl oz) bottle clam juice**
3 ml	**(¾ tsp) dried thyme**
2 ml	**(½ tsp) salt**
▲ 500 g	**(1 lb) halibut or other firm white fish, cut into 2.5 cm (1 inch) chunks**
▲ 1	**425 ml (14 ½ fl oz) can diced tomatoes**
30 ml	**(2 Tbsp) chopped fresh parsley**

1. Heat oil in large saucepan over medium heat. Add onion and celery; cook, stirring, until softened, about 5 minutes. Add potatoes, broth, clam juice, thyme, and salt; bring to boil. Reduce heat and simmer, partially covered, until potatoes are almost tender, about 8 minutes.

2. Add halibut and tomatoes to pot. Simmer, partially covered, stirring occasionally, until fish is just opaque in centre, about 5 minutes. Stir in parsley.

PER SERVING (375 ML [1 ½ CUPS]): 519 grams, 284 Cal, 6 g Total Fat, 1 g Sat Fat, 0 g Trans Fat, 36 mg Chol, 665 mg Sod, 30 g Total Carb, 7 g Total Sugar, 5 g Fib, 29 g Prot, 103 mg Calc.

FYI A **chowder** is a thick and chunky soup that often contains seafood. The word "chowder" comes from the French word *chaudière*, which was the caldron that fishermen used when making soup.

Tuscan-Style Bean Soup

LEVEL Basic

PREP 15 min

COOK 10 min

SERVES 4

10 ml	**(2 tsp) olive oil**
▲ 1	**onion, chopped**
▲ 1	**carrot, diced**
▲ 1	**celery stalk, diced**
2	**garlic cloves, minced**
▲ 1	**475 ml (15 ½ fl oz) can cannellini (white kidney) beans, rinsed and drained**
▲ 500 ml	**(2 cups) reduced-sodium chicken broth**
▲ 2	**plum tomatoes, seeded and diced**
60 ml	**(¼ cup) thinly sliced fresh basil**
1 ml	**(¼ tsp) black pepper**
60 ml	**(¼ cup) grated Parmesan cheese**

1. Heat oil in medium saucepan over medium heat. Add onion, carrot, and celery; cook, stirring, until onion is softened, about 5 minutes. Add garlic and cook, stirring, until fragrant, about 30 seconds. Stir in beans and broth. With potato masher, coarsely mash cannellini beans.

2. Stir tomatoes, basil, and pepper into soup; bring to boil. Reduce heat and simmer, stirring occasionally, until heated through, about 4 minutes. Serve sprinkled with Parmesan.

PER SERVING (250 ML [1 CUP]): 303 grams, 139 Cal, 4 g Total Fat, 1 g Sat Fat, 0 g Trans Fat, 4 mg Chol, 517 mg Sod, 18 g Total Carb, 5 g Total Sugar, 5 g Fib, 8 g Prot, 115 mg Calc.

▲ **HEALTHY EXTRA** Chop a 125 g (4 oz) piece of cooked lean ham and stir it into the soup along with the tomatoes in step 2. This will increase the per-serving *PointsPlus* value by *1*.

Tuscan-Style
Bean Soup

3

Dinner

Mustard and Herb-Rubbed Beef
with Winter Vegetables

Mustard and Herb-Rubbed Beef with Winter Vegetables

8
PointsPlus®
value
Per Serving

LEVEL Basic
PREP 25 min
ROAST 1 hr 30 min
SERVES 8

30 ml	**(2 Tbsp) chopped fresh thyme**
2	**garlic cloves, minced**
30 ml	**(2 Tbsp) Dijon mustard**
20 ml	**(4 tsp) olive oil**
2 ml	**(½ tsp) black pepper**
▲ 1 kg	**(2 lb) boneless eye of round roast, trimmed**
15 ml	**(1 Tbsp) water**
▲ 1 kg	**(2 lb) small Yukon Gold potatoes, scrubbed and halved**
▲ 500 g	**(1 lb) carrots, cut on diagonal into 5 cm (2 inch) lengths**
▲ 500 g	**(1 lb) parsnips, cut on diagonal into 5 cm (2 inch) lengths**
▲ 1	**onion, cut into wedges**

1. Preheat oven to 230°C (450°F). Spray very large roasting pan with nonstick spray.

2. Stir together thyme, garlic, mustard, oil, and pepper in small bowl. Place beef roast in prepared roasting pan. Rub half of herb mixture on top and sides of beef.

3. Stir water into remaining herb mixture until blended. Combine potatoes, carrots, parsnips, and onion in large bowl. Add herb mixture and toss to coat evenly. Scatter vegetables around meat.

4. Put roast in oven and reduce temperature to 180°C (350°F). Roast, stirring vegetables occasionally, until vegetables are tender and instant-read thermometer inserted into centre of roast registers 60°C (140°F) for medium, about 1 hour 30 minutes. Transfer roast to cutting board; let stand 10 minutes. Thinly slice across grain into 24 slices

PER SERVING (3 SLICES BEEF AND ⅛ OF VEGETABLES): 326 grams, 323 Cal, 7 g Total Fat, 2 g Sat Fat, 1 g Trans Fat, 52 mg Chol, 183 mg Sod, 39 g Total Carb, 8 g Total Sugar, 6 g Fib, 26 g Prot, 52 mg Calc.

FYI Spreading the herb mixture over the beef several hours ahead will make the roast even more flavourful. Loosely cover the roast with foil or plastic wrap and refrigerate until you're ready to pop it into the oven. Remove the foil before roasting.

Roasted Garlic-Rubbed Sirloin Steak

4 PointsPlus® value

Per Serving

LEVEL Basic

PREP 15 min

ROAST/BROIL 25 min

SERVES 4

5	**large garlic cloves, unpeeled**
5 ml	**(1 tsp) dried basil**
2 ml	**(½ tsp) dried oregano**
2 ml	**(½ tsp) salt**
2 ml	**(½ tsp) black pepper**
▲ 1	**500 g (1 lb) boneless sirloin steak, trimmed**

1. Preheat oven to 200°C (400°F).

2. Loosely wrap garlic in foil and place in small baking dish. Roast until softened, about 15 minutes. Unwrap carefully.

3. When cool enough to handle, squeeze soft garlic from each clove into small bowl. Add basil, oregano, salt, and pepper, stirring until blended. Rub over both sides of steak.

4. Spray broiler rack with nonstick spray. Preheat broiler.

5. Place steak on prepared broiler rack. Broil 12.5 cm (5 inches) from heat until instant-read thermometer inserted into centre of steak registers 60°C (140°F) for medium, about 5 minutes per side. Transfer steak to cutting board and let stand 5 minutes. Slice across grain into 12 slices.

PER SERVING (3 SLICES): 76 grams, 151 Cal, 6 g Total Fat, 2 g Sat Fat, 1 g Trans Fat, 63 mg Chol, 338 mg Sod, 2 g Total Carb, 0 g Total Sugar, 0 g Fib, 22 g Prot, 26 mg Calc.

▲ HEALTHY EXTRA Round out this meal by serving steamed spinach and baked potatoes alongside. A 200 g (7 oz) baked potato with each serving will increase the *PointsPlus* value by *4*.

Hearty Beef-Bulgur Loaf

LEVEL Basic
PREP 20 min
BAKE 30 min
SERVES 4

125 ml (½ cup) warm water
▲ 75 ml (⅓ cup) fine bulgur
▲ 60 ml (¼ cup) moist-packed sun-dried tomatoes (not packed in oil), chopped
▲ 500 g (1 lb) ground lean beef (5% fat or less)
▲ 75 ml (⅓ cup) plain fat-free yogourt
▲ 1 small onion, finely chopped
1 garlic clove, minced
▲ 1 large egg white
2 ml (½ tsp) dried oregano
2 ml (½ tsp) salt
1 ml (¼ tsp) black pepper

1. Preheat oven to 190°C (375°F). Spray 10 x 20 cm (4 x 8 inch) loaf pan with nonstick spray.

2. Stir together water, bulgur, and sun-dried tomatoes in large bowl; let soak 10 minutes.

3. Add remaining ingredients to bulgur mixture, stirring to mix well. Press mixture into prepared loaf pan. Bake until instant-read thermometer inserted into centre of loaf registers 70°C (160°F) for well done, about 30 minutes. Let stand 10 minutes. Cut into 8 slices.

PER SERVING (2 SLICES): 169 grams, 214 Cal, 6 g Total Fat, 2 g Sat Fat, 1 g Trans Fat, 63 mg Chol, 439 mg Sod, 14 g Total Carb, 3 g Total Sugar, 3 g Fib, 27 g Prot, 48 mg Calc.

FYI **Bulgur** is whole wheat that has been steamed, dried, and ground to a fine, medium, or coarse texture. When soaked in warm water, it develops a chewy texture and tempting nutty flavour. Bulgur is a staple in Middle Eastern salads, stews, and side dishes, such as tabbouleh.

North African Meatball Stew

5 PointsPlus© value ™
Per Serving

LEVEL Basic
PREP 20 min
COOK 35 min
SERVES 4

▲ 500 g (1 lb ground lean beef (5% fat or less)

30 ml (2 Tbsp) finely chopped fresh cilantro

10 ml (2 tsp) ground cumin

2 ml (½ tsp) salt

1 ml (¼ tsp) black pepper

10 ml (2 tsp) olive oil

▲ 1 onion, chopped

2 garlic cloves, minced

▲ 250 ml (1 cup) diced tomatoes

175 ml (¾ cup) water

▲ 45 ml (3 Tbsp) tomato paste

30 ml (2 Tbsp) lemon juice

30 ml (2 Tbsp) chopped fresh mint

1. Mix together beef, cilantro, 5 ml (1 tsp) of cumin, 1 ml (¼ tsp) of salt, and 0.5 ml (⅛ tsp) of pepper in large bowl just until well combined. With damp hands, shape mixture into 24 (2.5 cm (1 inch) diameter) meatballs.

2. Heat oil in large nonstick skillet over medium heat. Add onion and cook, stirring, until softened, about 5 minutes. Add garlic and cook, stirring, until fragrant, about 30 seconds. Stir in tomatoes, water, tomato paste, and remaining 5 ml (1 tsp) cumin, 1 ml (¼ tsp) salt, and 0.5 (⅛ tsp) pepper; bring to boil.

3. Add meatballs to skillet. Reduce heat and simmer, covered, until meatballs are cooked through and sauce is thickened, about 30 minutes. Stir in lemon juice and sprinkle with mint.

PER SERVING (6 MEATBALLS AND ABOUT 150 ML [⅔ CUP] SAUCE): 276 grams, 217 Cal, 8 g Total Fat, 3 g Sat Fat, 1 g Trans Fat, 62 mg Chol, 434 mg Sod, 11 g Total Carb, 6 g Total Sugar, 3 g Fib, 25 g Prot, 44 mg Calc.

▲ **HEALTHY EXTRA** Serve this stew with a bowl of couscous (150 ml [⅔ cup] of cooked whole wheat couscous with each serving will increase the *PointsPlus* value by *3*).

North African Meatball Stew

Grilled Asian-Flavoured Pork Skewers

8
PointsPlus®
value

Per Serving

LEVEL Basic

PREP 25 min

GRILL 10 min

SERVES 4

125 ml	(½ cup) water water
45 ml	**(3 Tbsp) reduced-sodium soy sauce**
30 ml	**(2 Tbsp) honey**
30 ml	**(2 Tbsp) lime juice**
3	**garlic cloves, minced**
▲ **500 g**	**(1 lb) lean pork tenderloin, trimmed and cut into 16 slices**
▲ **16**	**white mushrooms**
▲ **16**	**cherry tomatoes**
▲ **500 ml**	**(2 cups) hot cooked brown basmati rice**
10 ml	**(2 tsp) sesame seeds, toasted**

1. Combine water, soy sauce, honey, lime juice, and garlic in large zip-close plastic bag; add pork. Squeeze out air and seal bag; turn to coat pork. Refrigerate, turning bag occasionally, at least 30 minutes or up to 6 hours.

2. Spray grill rack with nonstick spray. Preheat grill to medium-high or prepare medium-high fire using direct method.

3. Alternately thread pork, mushrooms, and tomatoes onto 8 (30 cm [12 inch] metal) skewers. Place skewers on grill rack and grill until pork is cooked through and vegetables are tender, about 4 minutes per side.

4. Sprinkle rice with sesame seeds and serve with pork.

PER SERVING (2 SKEWERS AND 125 ML [½ CUP] RICE): 276 grams, 324 Cal, 6 g Total Fat, 2 g Sat Fat, 0 g Trans Fat, 75 mg Chol, 175 mg Sod, 40 g Total Carb, 5 g Total Sugar, 3 g Fib, 29 g Prot, 13 mg Calc.

FYI The **easiest way to cut raw pork** into uniform slices is to first freeze it until firm, which will take about 30 minutes.

Mexican-Style Pork Stew

LEVEL Basic

PREP 15 min

COOK 1 hr 15 min

SERVES 4

5 ml	**(1 tsp) canola oil**
3	**garlic cloves, minced**
250 ml	**(1 cup) water**
60 ml	**(¼ cup) cider vinegar**
60 ml	**(¼ cup) ancho chile powder**
5 ml	**(1 tsp) dried oregano**
1 ml	**(¼ tsp) salt**
▲ 500 g	**(1 lb) boneless centre-cut lean pork loin, trimmed and cut into 3.5 cm (1 ½ inch) chunks**
▲ 500 ml	**(2 cups) hot cooked brown rice**
▲ 125	**(½ cup) fat-free salsa**

1. Heat oil in small saucepan over medium heat. Add garlic and cook, stirring, until fragrant, about 30 seconds. Stir in water, vinegar, chile powder, oregano, and salt until mixed well. Bring to boil. Reduce heat and simmer 10 minutes.

2. Transfer chile mixture to Dutch oven or large saucepan; stir in pork and bring to boil. Reduce heat and gently simmer, covered, until meat is very tender, about 1 hour. Serve with rice and salsa.

PER SERVING (SCANT 250 ML [1 CUP] PORK WITH SAUCE, 125 ML [½ CUP] RICE, AND 30 ML [2 TBSP] SALSA): 294 grams, 329 Cal, 11 g Total Fat, 3 g Sat Fat, 0 g Trans Fat, 63 mg Chol, 474 mg Sod, 33 g Total Carb, 5 g Total Sugar, 5 g Fib, 27 g Prot, 84 mg Calc.

FYI This stew's great flavour comes from the adobo sauce in which it is cooked. In Mexico, adobo is made with chiles, vinegar, and herbs. Ancho chiles, used in our adobo sauce, are the most commonly used chiles in Mexican cooking. They are the "sweetest" of all the dried chiles, with a flavour reminiscent of coffee, licorice, and raisins. Ancho chiles are available dried and ground in supermarkets and specialty food stores.

**Broiled Lamb Kebabs
with Spinach-Lentil Salad**

Broiled Lamb Kebabs with Spinach-Lentil Salad

8 PointsPlus© value
Per Serving

LEVEL Basic
PREP 15 min
COOK/BROIL 30 min
SERVES 4

1 L	**(4 cups) water**
▲ 250 ml	**(1 cup) red lentils, picked over, rinsed, and drained**
30 ml	**(2 Tbsp) lemon juice**
10 ml	**(2 tsp) olive oil**
2 ml	**(½ tsp) salt**
1 ml	**(¼ tsp) black pepper**
500 g	**(1 lb) boneless lean lamb loin, trimmed and cut into 2.5 cm (1 inch) chunks**
3 ml	**(¾ tsp) dried oregano**
12	**cherry tomatoes**
▲ 500 ml	**(2 cups) lightly packed coarsely chopped spinach**
▲ 1	**small orange bell pepper, chopped**
▲ ½	**small red onion, thinly sliced**

1. Combine water and lentils in large saucepan; bring to boil. Reduce heat and simmer, covered, until lentils are tender, about 15 minutes; drain.

2. Meanwhile, to make dressing, whisk together lemon juice, oil, 1 ml (¼ tsp) of salt, and 0.5 ml (⅛ tsp) of black pepper in large bowl.

3. Spray broiler rack with nonstick spray. Preheat broiler.

4. Toss together lamb, oregano, and remaining 1 ml (¼ tsp) salt and 0.5 ml (⅛ tsp) black pepper in large bowl to coat evenly. Thread lamb and tomatoes evenly onto 4 (30 cm [12 inch]) metal skewers. Broil 12.5 cm (5 inches) from heat, turning, until lamb is cooked through and tomatoes are softened, about 8 minutes.

5. Add lentils, spinach, bell pepper, and onion to dressing; toss until mixed well. Spoon lentil salad onto platter and top with kebabs.

PER SERVING (1 KEBAB AND 175 ML [¾ CUP] LENTIL SALAD): 400 grams, 324 Cal, 8 g Total Fat, 2 g Sat Fat, 1 g Trans Fat, 65 mg Chol, 382 mg Sod, 31 g Total Carb, 3 g Total Sugar, 8 g Fib, 32 g Prot, 67 mg Calc.

▲ **HEALTHY EXTRA** Cook 2 carrots, cut into small dice, along with the lentils in step 1.

Lamb, Bacon, and Bean Chili

LEVEL Basic

PREP 15 min

COOK 1 hr 30 min

SERVES 6

3	slices turkey bacon
10 ml	(2 tsp) olive oil
500 g	(1 lb) boneless lean lamb loin, trimmed and cut into 1.25 cm (½-inch) pieces
▲ 1	onion, chopped
2	garlic cloves, minced
15 ml	(1 Tbsp) chili powder
10 ml	(2 tsp) ground cumin
▲ 1	796 ml (28 fl oz) can crushed tomatoes
1	teaspoon dried oregano
▲ 1	475 ml (15 ½ fl oz) can pinto beans, rinsed and drained

1. Cook bacon in Dutch oven until crisp. Transfer to paper towels to drain. Wipe pot clean.

2. Heat 5 ml (1 tsp) of oil in Dutch oven over medium-high heat. Add lamb, in batches, and cook until lightly browned on all sides, about 10 minutes, transferring lamb to plate as it is browned.

3. Add remaining 5 ml (1 tsp) oil to pot. Add onion and cook, stirring, until softened, about 5 minutes. Add the garlic, chili powder, and cumin; cook, stirring, until fragrant, about 30 seconds. Stir in tomatoes and oregano; bring to boil. Reduce heat and simmer, covered, until lamb is very tender, about 1 hour. Stir in beans and simmer until heated through, about 5 minutes longer.

PER SERVING (250 ML [1 CUP]): 267 grams, 227 Cal, 7 g Total Fat, 2 g Sat Fat, 1 g Trans Fat, 50 mg Chol, 422 mg Sod, 20 g Total Carb, 6 g Total Sugar, 6 g Fib, 20 g Prot, 85 mg Calc.

▲ **HEALTHY EXTRA** Serve this robust chili over 150 ml (⅔ cup) cooked quinoa. Per serving will increase the *PointsPlus* value by *3*.

Shepherd's Pie

6 PointsPlus® value

Per Serving

LEVEL Basic

PREP 25 min

COOK/BAKE 1 hr 10 min

SERVES 6

▲ **750 g** **(1 ½ lb) Yukon Gold potatoes, peeled and cut into chunks**

▲ **125 ml** **(½ cup) plain fat-free yogourt**

30 ml **(2 Tbsp) finely chopped fresh parsley**

3 ml **(¾ tsp) salt**

2 ml **(½ tsp) black pepper**

10 ml **(2 tsp) olive oil**

▲ **1** **large onion, chopped**

▲ **250 g** **(½ lb) ground lean beef (5% fat or less)**

250 g **(½ lb) ground lean lamb**

▲ **1** **425 ml (14 ½ fl oz) can diced tomatoes**

▲ **250 ml** **(1 cup) frozen baby peas**

2 ml **(½ tsp) dried thyme**

1. Preheat oven to 190°C (375°F).

2. Put potatoes in large saucepan and add enough water to cover. Bring to boil. Reduce heat and simmer, partially covered, until potatoes are tender, about 20 minutes; drain. With potato masher, mash potatoes until smooth; stir in yogourt, parsley, 2 ml (½ tsp) of salt, and 1 ml (¼ tsp) of pepper.

3. Heat oil in large nonstick skillet over medium heat. Add onion; cook, stirring, until softened, about 5 minutes. Add beef and lamb; cook, breaking meat apart with spoon, until browned, about 7 minutes. Drain off fat.

4. Add tomatoes, peas, thyme, and remaining 1 ml (¼ tsp) salt and 1 ml (¼ tsp) pepper to skillet; bring to boil. Reduce heat and simmer, stirring occasionally, 10 minutes.

5. Spread meat mixture in 25 cm (10 inch) deep-dish pie plate or 1.5 L (1 ½ quart) baking dish. Spread mashed potatoes on top. Bake until potatoes begin to brown and filling is bubbly, about 20 minutes. Let stand 10 minutes before serving.

PER SERVING (GENEROUS 250ML [1 CUP]): 304 grams, 255 Cal, 5 g Total Fat, 2 g Sat Fat, 0 g Trans Fat, 43 mg Chol, 452 mg Sod, 33 g Total Carb, 8 g Total Sugar, 5 g Fib, 20 g Prot, 65 mg Calc.

FYI **Shepherd's pie** was originally created as a way to use up leftovers from the traditional English Sunday roast.

Crispiest Oven-Fried Chicken

5 PointsPlus® value

Per Serving

LEVEL Basic
PREP 15 min
BAKE 35 min
SERVES 6

75 ml	**(⅓ cup) fat-free mayonnaise**
15 ml	**(1 Tbsp) Dijon mustard**
2	**garlic cloves, minced**
2 ml	**(½ tsp) salt**
1 ml	**(¼ tsp) hot pepper sauce or to taste**
▲ **3**	**375 g (¾ lb) bone-in chicken breasts, skinned and cut crosswise in half**
175 ml	**(¾ cup) cornflake crumbs**

1. Preheat oven to 190°C (375°F). Spray jelly-roll pan with nonstick spray.

2. Stir together mayonnaise, mustard, garlic, salt, and pepper sauce in large bowl. Add chicken and toss to coat evenly.

3. Put cornflake crumbs in large zip-close plastic bag. Add chicken, one piece at a time, and shake to coat; place chicken in prepared baking pan.

4. Lightly spray chicken with nonstick spray. Bake until golden brown and cooked through, about 35 minutes.

PER SERVING (1 PIECE CHICKEN): 109 grams, 186 Cal, 4 g Total Fat, 1 g Sat Fat, 0 g Trans Fat, 69 mg Chol, 507 mg Sod, 11 g Total Carb, 2 g Total Sugar, 0 g Fib, 26 g Prot, 18 mg Calc.

FYI If you happen to have **cornflakes** in your pantry, you can easily turn them into crumbs. Put them in a large zip-close plastic bag. Seal the bag, squeezing out the air, and roll over the crumbs with a rolling pin until crushed. You'll need approximately 500 ml (2 cups) cornflakes to yield 175 ml (¾ cup) crumbs.

Rosemary Chicken with Cherry Tomato Sauce

5 PointsPlus value

Per Serving

LEVEL Basic

PREP 15 min

COOK 15 min

SERVES 4

▲ 4	**150 g (5 oz) skinless boneless chicken breasts**
15 ml	**(1 Tbsp) chopped fresh rosemary, thyme, or oregano**
2 ml	**(½ tsp) salt**
1 ml	**(¼ tsp) black pepper**
10 ml	**(2 tsp) olive oil**
1	**large shallot, minced**
2	**garlic cloves, minced**
▲ 500 ml	**(1 pint) cherry tomatoes, halved**
▲ 60 ml	**(¼ cup) reduced-sodium vegetable broth**
60 ml	**(¼ cup) chopped fresh basil**

1. Place chicken between two pieces of plastic wrap. With meat pounder or rolling pin, pound to even thickness.

2. Sprinkle chicken with rosemary, salt, and pepper. Heat oil in large nonstick skillet over medium heat. Add chicken and cook until browned and cooked through, about 4 minutes per side. Transfer chicken to platter. Keep warm.

3. Add shallot and garlic to skillet. Cook, stirring, until softened, about 3 minutes. Add tomatoes and broth; cook, stirring occasionally, until tomatoes begin to soften, about 4 minutes longer. Stir in basil. Spoon sauce over chicken.

PER SERVING (1 CHICKEN BREAST AND ABOUT 125 ML [½ CUP] SAUCE): 194 grams, 197 Cal, 6 g Total Fat, 1 g Sat Fat, 0 g Trans Fat, 78 mg Chol, 396 mg Sod, 5 g Total Carb, 0 g Total Sugar, 1 g Fib, 30 g Prot, 30 mg Calc.

▲ **HEALTHY EXTRA** A bowl of whole wheat pasta, such as spaghetti or penne, is the perfect side for our Italian-inspired chicken dish. Be sure to spoon a little of the tomato sauce over the pasta. Adding 175 ml (¾ cup) of cooked whole wheat pasta per serving will increase the *PointsPlus* value by *3*.

Grilled Chicken and Asparagus with Capers and Basil

LEVEL Basic
PREP 20 min
COOK 10 min
SERVES 4

▲ 4   **150 g (5 oz) skinless boneless chicken breasts**

5 ml   **(1 tsp) ground coriander**

2 ml   **(½ tsp) salt**

1 ml   **(¼ tsp) black pepper**

▲ 1   **500 g (1 lb) bunch asparagus, trimmed**

5 ml   **(1 tsp) olive oil**

▲ 1   **red onion, cut into wedges**

15 ml   **(1 Tbsp) capers, rinsed**

30 ml   **(2 Tbsp) sliced fresh basil**

Zest of ½ lemon

1. Spray grill rack with nonstick spray. Preheat grill to medium-high or prepare medium-high fire.

2. Sprinkle chicken with coriander, 1 ml (¼ tsp) of salt and the pepper. Place chicken on grill rack and grill, turning frequently until browned and cooked through, 8-10 minutes.

3. Toss together asparagus, oil, and remaining 1 ml (¼ tsp) salt until coated evenly. Spray onion with nonstick spray. Place asparagus and onion on grill rack and grill, turning often, until tender and well marked, about 4 minutes.

4. Toss together capers, basil, and lemon zest. Top chicken evenly with caper mixture and serve with asparagus and onion.

PER SERVING (1 CHICKEN BREAST AND ¼ OF ASPARAGUS AND ONION): 183 grams, 190 Cal, 5 g Total Fat, 1 g Sat Fat, 0 g Trans Fat, 78 mg Chol, 430 mg Sod, 5 g Total Carb, 0 g Total Sugar, 2 g Fib, 31 g Prot, 0 g Alcohol, 0 g Sugar Alcohol, 38 mg Calc.

▲ **HEALTHY EXTRA** Serve with a 150 ml (⅔ cup) bowl of cooked quinoa per serving will increase the *PointsPlus* value by *3*.

**Grilled Chicken and Asparagus
with Capers and Basil**

Easy Herbed Chicken Tenders

4 PointsPlus® value

Per Serving

LEVEL Basic

PREP 15 min

COOK 5 min

SERVES 4

15 ml	(1 Tbsp) olive oil
5 ml	(1 tsp) dried thyme
5 ml	(1 tsp) dried oregano
5 ml	(1 tsp) dried basil
5 ml	(1 tsp) dried sage
2 ml	(½ tsp) salt
2 ml	(¼ tsp) black pepper
▲ 500 g	(1 lb) chicken tenders

1. Stir together all ingredients except chicken in cup. Put chicken in large bowl; spread herb mixture all over chicken.

2. Spray nonstick ridged grill pan with nonstick spray and set over medium-high heat. Add chicken and cook until golden brown and cooked through, about 3 minutes per side.

PER SERVING (¼ OF CHICKEN): 79 grams, 155 Cal, 6 g Total Fat, 1 g Sat Fat, 0 g Trans Fat, 63 mg Chol, 346 mg Sod, 1 g Total Carb, 0 g Total Sugar, 1 g Fib, 23 g Prot, 35 mg Calc.

▲ **HEALTHY EXTRA** Serve a salad of sliced fennel, orange slices, and thinly sliced red onion, drizzled with balsamic vinegar alongside the chicken.

Chicken Thighs with Spinach and Mushrooms

LEVEL Basic
PREP 15 min
COOK 25 min
SERVES 6

1	250 g (8 oz) package no-yolk wide egg noodles
500 g	(1 lb) skinless boneless chicken thighs, trimmed and cut into 5 cm (2 inch) chunks
2 ml	(½ tsp) salt
1 ml	(¼ tsp) black pepper
5 ml	(1 tsp) olive oil
▲ 1	250 g (8 oz) package white mushrooms, sliced
▲ 1	onion, chopped
▲ 375 g	(¾ lb) plum tomatoes, seeded and chopped
▲ 375 ml	(1 ½ cups) reduced-sodium chicken broth
▲ 1	bunch baby spinach
60 ml	(¼ cup) low-fat (1%) milk
45 ml	(3 Tbsp) grated Parmesan cheese

1. Cook egg noodles according to package directions, omitting salt if desired; drain. Keep warm.

2. Meanwhile, sprinkle chicken with 1 ml (¼ tsp) of salt and 0.5 ml (⅛ tsp) of pepper. Heat oil in large nonstick skillet over medium-high heat. Add chicken and cook, turning, until browned. Transfer to plate.

3. Add mushrooms and onion to skillet; cook, stirring, until mushrooms release their liquid, about 5 minutes. Return chicken to skillet. Stir in tomatoes, broth, and remaining 1 ml (¼ tsp) salt and 0.5 ml (⅛ tsp) pepper; bring to boil. Reduce heat and simmer, stirring, until chicken is cooked through, about 10 minutes.

4. Stir spinach, milk, and Parmesan into chicken mixture. Cook, stirring, until spinach is wilted. Serve over noodles.

PER SERVING (ABOUT 375 ML [1 ½ CUPS]):
344 grams, 328 Cal, 8 g Total Fat, 2 g Sat Fat, 0 g Trans Fat, 53 mg Chol, 558 mg Sod, 41 g Total Carb, 7 g Total Sugar, 5 g Fib, 25 g Prot, 110 mg Calc.

Feta-Stuffed Chicken Breasts

Feta-Stuffed Chicken Breasts

4 PointsPlus® value
Per Serving

LEVEL Intermediate

PREP 25 min

BAKE 25 min

SERVES 4

▲ **60 g** **(2 oz) fat-free feta cheese, crumbled**

▲ **2** **moist-packed sun-dried tomatoes (not packed in oil), finely chopped**

4 **large fresh basil leaves, chopped**

1 ml **(¼ tsp) salt**

1 ml **(¼ tsp) black pepper**

60 ml **(¼ cup) panko (Japanese bread crumbs)**

▲ **4** **150 g (5 oz) skinless boneless chicken breasts**

20 ml **(4 tsp) fat-free mayonnaise**

1. Preheat oven to 220°C (425°F). Spray nonstick baking pan with nonstick spray.

2. With fork, mix together feta, sun-dried tomatoes, basil, salt, and pepper in small bowl until blended. Spread panko on sheet of wax paper.

3. With small sharp knife, cut pocket, about 6 cm (2 ½ inches) long, in each chicken breast. Put one-fourth of cheese mixture into each pocket; press edges closed. Brush top of each breast with mayonnaise. Press coated side of chicken, one breast at a time, in crumbs. Place, coated side up, in prepared baking pan.

4. Lightly spray crumbs with nonstick spray. Bake until chicken is cooked through and crust is golden, about 25 minutes.

PER SERVING (1 STUFFED CHICKEN BREAST):
117 grams, 187 Cal, 4 g Total Fat, 1 g Sat Fat, 0 g Trans Fat, 79 mg Chol, 508 mg Sod, 5 g Total Carb, 1 g Total Sugar, 0 g Fib, 32 g Prot, 67 mg Calc.

▲ **HEALTHY EXTRA** Spray a skillet with nonstick spray and cook sliced white mushrooms and baby spinach until the mushrooms are softened and the spinach is wilted. Serve alongside the chicken.

Chinese-Style Barbecued Chicken

6 PointsPlus value ™ Per Serving

LEVEL Basic

PREP 15 min

BAKE 40 min

SERVES 6

▲ 1   **small onion, finely chopped**

75 ml   **(⅓ cup) ketchup**

30 ml   **(2 Tbsp) brown sugar**

30 ml   **(2 Tbsp) hoisin sauce**

30 ml   **(2 Tbsp) reduced-sodium soy sauce**

30 ml   **(2 Tbsp) dry sherry or dry vermouth**

2   **garlic cloves, minced**

6   **250 g (½ lb) whole chicken legs, skinned**

1. Preheat oven to 200°C (400°F). Line shallow baking pan with nonstick foil.

2. Stir together all ingredients except chicken in large bowl. Add chicken and toss to coat evenly.

3. Place chicken in prepared baking pan; brush any remaining sauce over chicken. Cover pan with foil; bake 20 minutes. Remove foil and bake until chicken is glazed and cooked through, about 20 minutes longer.

PER SERVING (1 CHICKEN LEG): 133 grams, 243 Cal, 9 g Total Fat, 2 g Sat Fat, 0 g Trans Fat, 96 mg Chol, 539 mg Sod, 11 g Total Carb, 6 g Total Sugar, 0 g Fib, 28 g Prot, 22 mg Calc.

▲ **HEALTHY EXTRA** Serve this finger lickin'–good chicken with a refreshing cucumber salad. Peel, halve, and seed 2 large cucumbers. Slice and sprinkle with unseasoned rice vinegar and a pinch of red pepper flakes.

Healthy Oils

Eat fat at every meal. It doesn't take much—a few chopped walnuts on your breakfast cereal, olive oil in your salad dressing at lunch, fatty fish (like tuna) for dinner—but it's wise to incorporate some fat into every meal to add flavour, aid in your body's absorption of fat-soluble vitamins, and feel satisfied.

Think about spreads. Instead of relying on mayo or cream cheese for sandwich spreads, try smearing mashed avocado or a heart-healthy nut butter (such as almond, cashew, hazelnut, or peanut) on your bread.

Put flaxseeds in your fridge. Whether you grind them yourself or buy them ground, keep flaxseeds around (refrigerated for optimum freshness) and sprinkle on cereal or salads or use it in homemade breads or pancake batter or as a crusty coating for salmon or chicken. Flaxseeds are rich in fibre and a good source of healthy omega-3 fatty acids.

Turkey Sausages with Warm Potato Salad

6
PointsPlus®
value
Per Serving

LEVEL Basic
PREP 15 min
COOK 35 min
SERVES 6

▲ **750 g** **(1 ½ lb) red potatoes, scrubbed and cut into 2.5 cm (1 inch) chunks**

45 ml **(3 Tbsp) dry vermouth or reduced-sodium chicken broth**

45 ml **(3 Tbsp) white wine vinegar**

15 **(1 Tbsp) extra-virgin olive oil**

15 **(1 Tbsp) coarse-grained Dijon mustard**

1 ml **(¼ tsp) black pepper**

▲ **250 g** **(1 cup) grape tomatoes, halved**

▲ **2** **scallions, finely chopped**

75 ml **(⅓ cup) chopped fresh parsley**

30 ml **(2 Tbsp) chopped fresh dill**

15 ml **(1 Tbsp) nonpareil (tiny) capers, drained and chopped**

6 **sweet or hot Italian-style turkey sausages**

1. Put potatoes in large saucepan and add enough water to cover. Bring to boil. Reduce heat and cook, covered, until potatoes are tender, about 15 minutes; drain well. Transfer hot potatoes to serving bowl and sprinkle with vermouth; toss to coat evenly. Set aside, tossing potatoes occasionally.

2. To make dressing, whisk together vinegar, oil, mustard, and pepper until blended. Drizzle over potatoes, tossing to mix well. Add tomatoes, scallions, parsley, dill, and capers; gently toss to mix well.

3. Heat nonstick ridged grill pan over medium-high heat. Add sausages and cook, turning, until nicely marked and cooked through, about 15 minutes. Serve with potato salad.

PER SERVING (1 SAUSAGE AND ABOUT 175 ML [¾ CUP] POTATO SALAD): 227 grams, 251 Cal, 10 g Total Fat, 3 g Sat Fat, 0 g Trans Fat, 0 mg Chol, 528 mg Sod, 26 g Total Carb, 3 g Total Sugar, 3 g Fib, 14 g Prot, 23 mg Calc.

▲ **HEALTHY EXTRA** Serve the sausages and potato salad with a bowl of steamed whole green beans.

Turkey Sausages with Warm Potato Salad

Lemony Arctic Char with Black Bean Salad

6 PointsPlus© value ™

Per Serving

LEVEL Basic
PREP 30 min
BROIL 5 min
SERVES 4

Grated zest of 1 lemon

60 ml	(¼ cup) lemon juice
15 ml	(1 Tbsp) olive oil
10 ml	(2 tsp) honey
2 ml	(½ tsp) salt
2 ml	(½ tsp) black pepper
▲ 4	125 g (¼ lb) arctic char fillets, skinned
▲ 1	475 ml (15 ½ fl oz) can black beans, rinsed and drained
▲ 500 ml	(2 cups) fresh or thawed frozen corn kernels
▲ 1	orange bell pepper, diced
▲ 125 ml	(½ cup) chopped red onion
60 ml	(¼ cup) chopped fresh cilantro

1. To make dressing, whisk together lemon zest and juice, oil, honey, salt, and black pepper in small bowl.

2. Transfer 45 ml (3 Tbsp) of dressing to large zip-close plastic bag; add arctic char. Squeeze out air and seal bag; turn to coat fish. Refrigerate, turning bag occasionally, about 30 minutes. Reserve remaining dressing.

3. To make black bean salad, toss together remaining ingredients and dressing in serving bowl.

4. Spray broiler rack with nonstick spray. Preheat broiler.

5. Remove arctic char from marinade; discard marinade. Place fish on prepared broiler rack. Broil 12.5 cm (5 inches) from heat until fish is just opaque in centre, about 3 minutes per side. Serve with black bean salad

PER SERVING (1 ARCTIC CHAR FILLET AND ABOUT 175 ML [¾ CUP] SALAD): 292 grams, 247 Cal, 5 g Total Fat, 1 g Sat Fat, 0 g Trans Fat, 71 mg Chol, 474 mg Sod, 31 g Total Carb, 4 g Total Sugar, 7 g Fib, 21 g Prot, 42 mg Calc.

FYI **Arctic char is similar to salmon.** It is mostly farm-raised, using ecologically-friendly methods, which puts it high on the sustainable seafood list.

Pepper-Crusted Arctic Char with Mango

LEVEL Basic

PREP 5 min

COOK 10 min

SERVES 4

▲ 4	**150 g (5 oz) arctic char fillets, skinned**
2 ml	**(½ tsp) salt**
45 ml	**(3 Tbsp) coarse black pepper**
▲ 1	**mango, peeled, pitted, and cut into 8 wedges**

1. Sprinkle arctic char with salt. Spread pepper on sheet of wax paper. Lightly press both sides of arctic char fillets into pepper to coat.

2. Spray nonstick ridged grill pan with nonstick spray and set over medium-high heat. Place arctic char and mango in grill pan and cook until fish is just opaque in centre and mango is marked, about 4 minutes per side for the fish and 1 minute per side for mango.

PER SERVING (1 ARCTIC CHAR FILLET AND 2 MANGO WEDGES): 171 grams, 164 Cal, 4 g Total Fat, 1 g Sat Fat, 0 g Trans Fat, 94 mg Chol, 360 mg Sod, 12 g Total Carb, 8 g Total Sugar, 2 g Fib, 20 g Prot, 0 g Alcohol, 0 g Sugar Alcohol, 36 mg Calc.

▲ **HEALTHY EXTRA** Round out this meal with baked potatoes and steamed broccoli florets. A 200 g (7 oz) baked potato with each serving will increase the *PointsPlus* value by *4*.

Cod with Puttanesca Sauce

Cod with Puttanesca Sauce

LEVEL Basic
PREP 15 min
COOK 30 min
SERVES 4

▲ **170 g** **(6 oz) whole wheat spaghetti**

10 ml **(2 tsp) olive oil**

3 **garlic cloves, minced**

▲ **1** **796 ml (28 fl oz) can whole tomatoes in puree with basil**

30 ml **(2 Tbsp) pitted Kalamata olives, chopped**

30 ml **(2 Tbsp) chopped fresh parsley**

15 ml **(1 Tbsp) nonpareil (tiny) capers, drained**

5 ml **(1 tsp) dried oregano**

2 ml **(½ tsp) red pepper flakes or to taste**

▲ **1** **500 g (1 lb) cod fillet or halibut steak, cut into 4 equal pieces**

1. Cook spaghetti according to package directions, omitting salt if desired. Drain and keep warm.

2. Meanwhile, heat oil in deep large skillet over medium heat. Add garlic and cook, stirring, until fragrant, about 30 seconds. Add tomatoes, olives, parsley, capers, oregano, and pepper flakes; bring to boil. Reduce heat and simmer, breaking up tomatoes with side of wooden spoon, until sauce is slightly thickened, about 10 minutes.

3. Add cod to skillet, spooning sauce over fish; simmer, covered, until cod is just opaque in centre, about 8 minutes.

4. Transfer spaghetti to serving bowl. Spoon some sauce over pasta. Serve with fish and remaining sauce.

PER SERVING (1 COD FILLET, 175 ML [¾ CUP] SPAGHETTI, AND 175 ML [¾ CUP] SAUCE):
406 grams, 305 Cal, 5 g Total Fat, 1 g Sat Fat, 0 g Trans Fat, 43 mg Chol, 552 mg Sod, 39 g Total Carb, 6 g Total Sugar, 7 g Fib, 26 g Prot, 77 mg Calc.

FYI **Capers** are the unopened flower buds of a spiny bush that grows all over the Mediterranean. The smallest capers are called nonpareil. Their bold flavour makes a little bit go a long way. Capers are available in supermarkets packed in small bottles alongside the olives and pickles.

Oven-Crisped Cod

LEVEL Basic
PREP 10 min
ROAST 10 min
SERVES 4

▲ 1   **500 g (1 lb) cod fillet or halibut steak, cut into 4 equal pieces**

60 ml   **(¼ cup) chopped fresh parsley**

Juice of 1 lemon

30 ml   **(2 Tbsp) all-purpose flour**

10 ml   **(2 tsp) olive oil**

2 ml   **(½ tsp) dried oregano**

2 ml   **(½ tsp) salt**

1 ml   **(¼ tsp) black pepper**

Pinch cayenne

1. Preheat oven to 230°C (450°F). Spray 18 x 28 cm (7 x 11 inch) baking dish with nonstick spray.

2. Place fish in prepared baking dish.

3. Mix together remaining ingredients in small bowl. Spoon flour mixture evenly over fish. Bake until fish is just opaque in centre and crisp on top, about 10 minutes.

PER SERVING (1 COD FILLET): 101 grams, 122 Cal, 3 g Total Fat, 1 g Sat Fat, 0 g Trans Fat, 43 mg Chol, 354 mg Sod, 4 g Total Carb, 1 g Total Sugar, 0 g Fib, 19 g Prot, 21 mg Calc.

▲ **HEALTHY EXTRA** Serve this crispy lemon-infused fish with a sliced tomato and red onion salad.

Tuna with Fennel, Orange, and Olive Salad

PointsPlus value 6 Per Serving

LEVEL Basic
PREP 25 min
COOK 5 min
SERVES 4

▲ 1   **large fennel bulb, very thinly sliced**

▲ 1   **navel orange, sectioned**

▲ 2   **scallions, chopped**

12   **pitted Kalamata olives, coarsely chopped**

60 ml   **(¼ cup) red wine vinegar**

20 ml   **(4 tsp) olive oil**

2 ml   **(½ tsp) salt**

1 ml   **(¼ tsp) black pepper**

▲ 4   **150 g (5 oz) tuna steaks, 2 cm (¾ inch) thick**

1. To make salad, toss together fennel, orange sections, scallions, olives, vinegar, 10 ml (2 tsp) oil, 1 ml (¼ tsp) of salt, and 0.5 ml (⅛ tsp) of pepper in serving bowl.

2. Sprinkle tuna with remaining 1 ml (¼ tsp) salt and 0.5 ml (⅛ tsp) pepper. Heat remaining 10 ml (2 tsp) oil in nonstick skillet over medium heat. Add tuna and cook until browned on outside but still pink in centre, about 3 minutes per side. Serve with fennel salad.

PER SERVING (1 TUNA STEAK AND ABOUT 250 ML [1 CUP] SALAD): 208 grams, 255 Cal, 9 g Total Fat, 1 g Sat Fat, 0 g Trans Fat, 66 mg Chol, 542 mg Sod, 7 g Total Carb, 4 g Total Sugar, 2 g Fib, 35 g Prot, 59 mg Calc.

FYI **To section an orange,** cut a slice off the top and bottom end. Stand the orange and slice off the peel and white pith, turning the orange as you cut. Hold the fruit over a bowl to catch the juices and cut between the membranes to release the sections, allowing the sections and juice to fall into the bowl.

Mushroom and Spinach–Stuffed Trout

7 PointsPlus® value ™ Per Serving

LEVEL Intermediate

PREP 30 min

COOK/BAKE 25 min

SERVES 4

10 ml	(2 tsp) olive oil
▲ 60 ml	(¼ lb) white mushrooms, chopped
▲ 1	onion, chopped
▲ 1	290 g (10 oz) package frozen chopped spinach, thawed and squeezed dry
125 ml	(½ cup) shredded reduced-fat Cheddar cheese
▲ 4	150 g (5 oz) skinless rainbow trout fillets
1 ml	(¼ tsp) salt
1 ml	(¼ tsp) black pepper
125 ml	(½ cup) fresh whole wheat bread crumbs (about 1 slice bread)

1. Preheat oven to 230°C (450°F). Spray 23 cm (9-inch) square baking dish with nonstick spray.

2. Heat oil in medium skillet over medium heat. Add mushrooms and onion; cook, stirring, until mushrooms release their liquid and it is evaporated, about 10 minutes. Stir in spinach and Cheddar.

3. Lay trout, skinned side up, on work surface; sprinkle with salt and pepper. Top fillets evenly with spinach mixture. Roll up fish and place, seam-side down, in prepared baking dish. Sprinkle bread crumbs evenly over fish; spray with nonstick spray.

4. Bake until trout is just opaque in centre and crumbs are golden, about 15 minutes.

PER SERVING (1 STUFFED TROUT FILLET):
272 grams, 286 Cal, 12 g Total Fat, 4 g Sat Fat, 0 g Trans Fat, 85 mg Chol, 418 mg Sod, 11 g Total Carb, 3 g Total Sugar, 4 g Fib, 33 g Prot, 288 mg Calc.

FYI This elegant dish is **ideal company food**. The fish can be prepared up to 8 hours ahead, then covered and refrigerated until ready to bake. Baked tomato halves or steamed asparagus make the perfect accompaniments.

Cajun-Seasoned Catfish

4 PointsPlus® value

Per Serving

LEVEL Basic
PREP 15 min
BAKE 10 min
SERVES 4

▲ **60 ml** **(¼ cup) yellow cornmeal**

45 ml **(3 Tbsp) all-purpose flour**

10 ml **(2 tsp) Cajun seasoning**

2 ml **(½ tsp) salt**

2 ml **(½ tsp) black pepper**

▲ **1** **large egg**

▲ **4** **125 g (¼ lb) catfish fillets**

1. Preheat oven to 230°C (450°F). Spray broiler pan or heavy baking sheet with nonstick spray.

2. Mix together cornmeal, flour, Cajun seasoning, salt, and pepper on sheet of wax paper.

3. Lightly beat egg in large shallow bowl or pie plate. Dip fish, one piece at a time, into egg, then coat in cornmeal mixture, pressing lightly so it adheres.

4. Place fish in prepared pan. Lightly spray with nonstick spray. Bake until just opaque in centre and crisp and golden on outside, about 10 minutes.

PER SERVING (1 CATFISH FILLET): 115 grams, 162 Cal, 4 g Total Fat, 1 g Sat Fat, 0 g Trans Fat, 114 mg Chol, 470 mg Sod, 12 g Total Carb, 0 g Total Sugar, 1 g Fib, 19 g Prot, 18 mg Calc.

▲ **HEALTHY EXTRA** Corn on the cob and a steamed dark green leafy vegetable, such as collard greens, mustard greens, or Swiss chard suit this fish to a tee. One medium ear of corn, grilled or steamed, with each serving will increase the *PointsPlus* value by *2*.

Shrimp and Chicken Jambalaya

LEVEL Basic
PREP 25 min
COOK 55 min
SERVES 6

10 ml	**(2 tsp) olive oil**
▲ **1**	**large onion, chopped**
▲ **1**	**red bell pepper, chopped**
▲ **1**	**celery stalk, chopped**
2	**garlic cloves, minced**
▲ **250 ml**	**(1 cup) brown rice**
▲ **1**	**425 ml (14 ½ fl oz) can reduced-sodium chicken broth**
▲ **1**	**425 ml (14 ½ fl oz) can diced tomatoes**
2 ml	**(½ tsp) dried thyme**
2 ml	**(½ tsp) salt**
0.5 ml	**(⅛ tsp) cayenne**
▲ **250 g**	**(½ lb) skinless boneless chicken breasts, cut into 2 cm (¾-inch) chunks**
▲ **250 g**	**(½ lb) medium shrimp, peeled and deveined**
▲ **1 L**	**(4 cups) small broccoli florets**
▲ **1**	**60 g (2 oz) piece cooked low-sodium fat-free ham, diced**
▲ **3**	**scallions, thinly sliced**

1. Heat oil in nonstick Dutch oven over medium heat. Add onion, bell pepper, and celery; cook, stirring, until softened, about 5 minutes. Stir in garlic and cook, stirring, until fragrant, about 30 seconds. Add rice and cook, stirring, 1 minute.

2. Add broth, tomatoes, thyme, salt, and cayenne to pot; bring to boil. Reduce heat and simmer, covered, until rice is almost tender, about 30 minutes.

3. Add chicken to pot. Cook, covered, 10 minutes. Stir in shrimp, broccoli, and ham. Cook, covered, until shrimp are just opaque, chicken is cooked through, and rice is tender, about 5 minutes longer. Serve sprinkled with scallions.

PER SERVING (⅙ OF JAMBALAYA): 415 grams, 265 Cal, 5 g Total Fat, 1 g Sat Fat, 0 g Trans Fat, 82 mg Chol, 662 mg Sod, 35 g Total Carb, 6 g Total Sugar, 6 g Fib, 22 g Prot, 79 mg Calc.

FYI **To save some prep time,** buy two 250 g (8 oz) packages of broccoli florets from the produce section of your supermarket.

Asparagus and Shrimp Stir-Fry

7 PointsPlus® value
Per Serving

LEVEL Basic

PREP 15 min

COOK 15 min

SERVES 6

▲ **250 ml** **(1 cup) reduced-sodium chicken broth**

30 ml **(2 Tbsp) reduced-sodium soy sauce**

15 ml **(1 Tbsp) cornstarch**

10 ml **(2 tsp) canola oil**

▲ **1** **500 g (1 lb) bunch asparagus, trimmed and cut into 3.5 cm (1 ½-inch) lengths**

▲ **2** **red bell peppers, thinly sliced**

▲ **500 g** **(1 lb) large shrimp, peeled and deveined, tails left on if desired**

▲ **1** **bunch scallions, trimmed and cut into 5 cm (2-inch) lengths**

30 ml **(2 Tbsp) minced peeled fresh ginger**

3 **garlic cloves, minced**

10 ml **(2 tsp) Asian (dark) sesame oil**

▲ **1 L** **(4 cups) hot cooked brown rice**

1. Stir together broth, soy sauce, and cornstarch in small bowl until smooth.

2. Heat nonstick wok or deep large nonstick skillet over medium-high heat until drop of water sizzles in pan; add oil and swirl to coat pan. Add asparagus and bell peppers; stir-fry until crisp-tender, about 5 minutes. Add shrimp and scallions; stir-fry until shrimp are just opaque in centre about 4 minutes. Add ginger and garlic; stir-fry until fragrant, about 1 minute.

3. Re-stir cornstarch mixture; add to wok along with sesame oil. Stir-fry until sauce bubbles and thickens, about 1 minute. Serve with rice.

PER SERVING (325 ML [1 ⅓ CUPS] SHRIMP WITH VEGETABLES AND 150 ML [⅔ CUP] RICE):
334 grams, 268 Cal, 5 g Total Fat, 1 g Sat Fat, 0 g Trans Fat, 112 mg Chol, 448 mg Sod, 38 g Total Carb, 3 g Total Sugar, 4 g Fib, 18 g Prot, 62 mg Calc.

FYI When it comes to **stir-fries**, preparing the ingredients takes more time than the actual cooking. Put all of the prepped ingredients in bowls alongside the stove for easy access.

Scallops with Tomatoes and Feta Cheese

LEVEL Basic
PREP 15 min
COOK/BROIL 25 min
SERVES 4

▲ 10 ml	**(2 tsp) olive oil**
▲ 1	**onion, chopped**
3	**garlic cloves, minced**
▲ 2	**large plum tomatoes, chopped**
75 ml	**(⅓ cup) dry white or red wine**
2 ml	**(½ tsp) dried oregano**
2 ml	**(½ tsp) salt**
1 ml	**(¼ tsp) black pepper**
▲ 500 g	**(1 lb) sea scallops**
15 ml	**(1 Tbsp) ouzo, pernod, or anisette**
60 g	**(2 oz) reduced-fat feta cheese, crumbled**
▲ 500 ml	**(2 cups) hot cooked brown rice**

1. Heat oil in large nonstick skillet over medium heat. Add onion and cook, stirring, until softened, about 5 minutes. Add garlic and cook, stirring, until fragrant, about 30 seconds. Add tomatoes, wine, oregano, salt, and pepper; bring to boil. Reduce heat and simmer, until flavours are blended, about 10 minutes.

2. Add scallops to tomato mixture; cook until just opaque in centre, about 5 minutes. Stir in ouzo.

3. Preheat broiler.

4. Turn scallop mixture into heatproof casserole dish. Sprinkle with feta. Broil 5 inches from heat until cheese is lightly browned and softened, about 2 minutes. Serve over rice.

PER SERVING (ABOUT 250 ML [1 CUP] SCALLOP MIXTURE AND 125 ML [½ CUP] RICE): 284 grams, 308 Cal, 8 g Total Fat, 2 g Sat Fat, 0 g Trans Fat, 39 mg Chol, 682 mg Sod, 33 g Total Carb, 5 g Total Sugar, 3 g Fib, 24 g Prot, 79 mg Calc.

> **FYI** Ouzo (OO-zoh), pernod (pehr-NOH), and anisette (an-ih-SEHT) are clear, sweet, anise-flavoured liqueurs that are often served as aperitifs. Ouzo is made in Greece, pernod is produced in France, and anisette is made in Italy.

Fisherman's Wharf Seafood Stew

Fisherman's Wharf Seafood Stew

LEVEL Basic

PREP 20 min

COOK 25 min

SERVES 6

10 ml	**(2 tsp) olive oil**
▲ 1	**red bell pepper, chopped**
▲ 6	**scallions, thinly sliced**
▲ 2	**celery stalks, chopped**
3	**garlic cloves, thinly sliced**
▲ 1	**425 ml (14 ½ fl oz) can diced tomatoes**
250 ml	**(1 cup) water**
250 ml	**(1 cup) dry white wine or dry vermouth**
	Pinch red pepper flakes
▲ 250 ml	**(1 cup) frozen corn kernels, thawed**
▲ 375 g	**(¾ lb) large shrimp, peeled and deveined, tails left on if desired**
▲ 250 g	**(½ lb) mussels, scrubbed and debearded**
▲ 250 g	**(½ lb) halibut fillet, cut into 3.5 cm (1 ½-inch) chunks**

1. Heat oil in nonstick Dutch oven over medium heat. Add bell pepper, scallions, celery, and garlic; cook, stirring, until softened, about 5 minutes. Add tomatoes, water, wine, and pepper flakes; bring to boil. Reduce heat and simmer, covered, until flavours are blended, about 10 minutes. Stir in corn.

2. Add shrimp, mussels, and halibut to pot; return to boil. Reduce heat and simmer, covered, until mussels open and shrimp are just opaque, about 5 minutes. Discard any mussels that do not open. Divide stew evenly among 6 large shallow soup bowls.

PER SERVING (325 ML [1 ⅓ CUPS]): 314 grams, 189 Cal, 4 g Total Fat, 1 g Sat Fat, 0 g Trans Fat, 106 mg Chol, 334 mg Sod, 14 g Total Carb, 4 g Total Sugar, 3 g Fib, 23 g Prot, 75 mg Calc.

Mussels in Saffron Tomato Broth

8 PointsPlus® value ™ Per Serving

LEVEL Basic
PREP 15 min
COOK 15 min
SERVES 5

1 ml	**(¼ tsp) saffron threads**
60 ml	**(¼ cup) hot water**
15 ml	**(1 Tbsp) olive oil**
75 ml	**(⅓ cup) minced shallots**
3	**garlic cloves, minced**
▲ **1**	**425 ml (14 ½ fl oz) can no salt added diced tomatoes**
125 ml	**(½ cup) dry white wine**
1 ml	**(¼ tsp) black pepper**
▲ **2 kg**	**(4 lb) mussels, scrubbed and debearded**
30 ml	**(2 Tbsp) chopped fresh parsley**

1. Stir together saffron and water in cup.

2. Heat oil in Dutch oven over medium heat. Add shallots and cook, stirring, until softened, about 4 minutes. Add garlic and cook, stirring, until fragrant, about 30 seconds.

3. Add tomatoes, wine, saffron water, and pepper to pot; bring to boil. Add mussels and simmer, covered, until they open, about 5 minutes, transferring mussels to large bowl as they open. Discard any mussels that do not open. Divide mussels evenly among 4 large, shallow bowls. Pour mussel broth over and sprinkle evenly with parsley.

PER SERVING (ABOUT 20 MUSSELS AND ABOUT 75 ML [⅓ CUP] BROTH): 440 grams, 333 Cal, 10 g Total Fat, 2 g Sat Fat, 0 g Trans Fat, 90 mg Chol, 951 mg Sod, 18 g Total Carb, 9 g Total Sugar, 2 g Fib, 39 g Prot, 107 mg Calc.

FYI The hairy filaments that protrude from **mussels** are known as the "beard." To remove it, pinch the beard between your fingers and firmly pull or cut it off with scissors. Debeard mussels just before cooking.

Living the Good Health Guidelines

Whole Grains

▶ **Fill up on fibre.** Aim to get 25–35 grams of fibre a day from whole grains, beans, peas, lentils, vegetables, and fruit by including at least one food from these categories in every meal and snack. Fibre increases your feeling of fullness and slows the time it takes food to pass through your digestive system.

▶ **Opt for whole wheat.** Whenever you have a choice of breads, tortillas, bagels, or pizza crusts, choose whole wheat or rye over the white-flour version. You'll get more in the way of flavour, the feeling of fullness, and nutrients from every bite.

▶ **Pack up your whole grains.** Place a reasonable portion of whole-grain crackers, air-popped popcorn, or whole-grain breakfast cereal (such as shredded wheat) and a few nuts in a sandwich bag and take it with you to replenish your energy and keep hunger at bay when you're on the run.

Two-Grain Stuffed Peppers

LEVEL Basic
PREP 25 min
COOK/BAKE/BROIL 1 hr
SERVES 4

10 ml	**(2 tsp) olive oil**
▲ 1	**onion, chopped**
250 ml	**(1 cup) water**
▲ 75 ml	**(⅓ cup) amaranth, rinsed**
75 ml	**(⅓ cup) white rice**
▲ 250 ml	**(1 cup) canned small white beans, rinsed and drained**
75 ml	**(⅓ cup) chopped fresh flat-leaf parsley**
▲ 1	**jalapeño pepper, seeded and minced**
1 ml	**(¼ tsp) salt**
1 ml	**(¼ tsp) black pepper**
▲ 2	**large bell peppers, cut in half through stem end and seeded**
60 g	**(2 oz) reduced-fat feta cheese, cut into 0.5 cm (¼-inch) dice**

1. Preheat oven to 180°C (350°F). Spray 20 x 30 cm (8 x 12 inch) baking dish with nonstick spray.

2. Heat oil in large nonstick saucepan over medium heat. Add onion and cook, stirring, until softened, about 5 minutes. Add water, amaranth, and rice; bring to boil. Reduce heat and simmer, covered, until amaranth and rice are tender and liquid is absorbed, about 20 minutes. Stir in beans, parsley, jalapeño, salt, and black pepper.

3. Divide amaranth mixture evenly among bell pepper halves; place in prepared baking dish. Cover dish tightly with foil; bake until bell peppers are tender and filling is heated through, about 30 minutes.

4. Preheat broiler.

5. Uncover baking dish. Sprinkle feta evenly over filling; broil 5 inches from heat until cheese is lightly browned and softened, about 3 minutes.

PER SERVING (1 STUFFED PEPPER HALF): 331 grams, 256 Cal, 5 g Total Fat, 2 g Sat Fat, 0 g Trans Fat, 5 mg Chol, 421 mg Sod, 43 g Total Carb, 5 g Total Sugar, 8 g Fib, 10 g Prot, 98 mg Calc.

FYI **Amaranth**, once thought of only as a common weed, is now appreciated as a nutritious high-protein grain. Amaranth greens can be used in soups and salads.

Vegetarian Moussaka

7 PointsPlus® value
Per Serving

LEVEL Intermediate
PREP 20 min
BAKE/COOK 50 min
SERVES 4

▲ 1   **500 g (1 lb) eggplant, unpeeled and cut into 0.5 cm (¼-inch) rounds**

10 ml   **(2 tsp) olive oil**

▲ 1   **onion, chopped**

3   **garlic cloves, minced**

▲ 1   **796 ml (28 fl oz) can whole tomatoes**

125 ml   **(½ cup) TVP (textured vegetable protein)**

▲ 1   **red bell pepper, chopped**

60 ml   **(¼ cup) dry white wine**

1 ml   **(¼ tsp) salt**

1 ml   **(¼ tsp) black pepper**

45 ml   **(3 Tbsp) all-purpose flour**

▲ 375 ml   **(1 ½ cups) fat-free milk**

▲ 1   **large egg**

0.5 ml   **(⅛ tsp) ground nutmeg**

125 ml   **(½ cup) grated Parmesan cheese**

1. Preheat oven to 190°C (375°F). Spray 20 x 30 cm (8 x 12 inch) baking dish with nonstick spray. Spray large baking sheet with nonstick spray.

2. Arrange eggplant slices on prepared baking sheet in single layer. Bake until softened, about 20 minutes.

3. Meanwhile, to make tomato sauce, heat oil in large nonstick saucepan over medium heat. Add onion and garlic; cook, stirring, until onion is golden, about 8 minutes. Add tomatoes with their juice, TVP, bell pepper, wine, salt, and black pepper; bring to boil. Reduce heat and simmer, breaking up tomatoes with side of wooden spoon, until liquid is almost evaporated, about 20 minutes.

4. To make white sauce, whisk together flour and 60 ml (¼ cup) of milk in small saucepan until smooth; whisk in remaining 310 ml (1 ¼ cups) milk. Cook over medium heat, stirring constantly, until mixture bubbles and thickens, about 3 minutes. Remove saucepan from heat. Beat egg and nutmeg in small bowl; stir about 125 ml (½ cup) of hot milk mixture into beaten egg, then stir into saucepan until mixed well.

5. Layer eggplant in prepared baking dish; spoon tomato sauce on top. Pour white sauce over and spread evenly; sprinkle with Parmesan. Bake until moussaka is heated through and top is golden, about 20 minutes. Let stand 5 minutes before serving.

PER SERVING (¼ OF MOUSSAKA): 523 grams, 291 Cal, 8 g Total Fat, 3 g Sat Fat, 0 g Trans Fat, 63 mg Chol, 764 mg Sod, 34 g Total Carb, 18 g Total Sugar, 9 g Fib, 23 g Prot, 367 mg Calc.

FYI   **TVP (textured vegetable protein) is dried, granular soybean meal that substitutes nicely for meat in vegetarian dishes. It is sold in bulk and in 500 g (1 lb) packages in supermarkets and natural health food stores.**

Broccoli-Polenta Casserole

LEVEL Basic

PREP 20 min

COOK/BAKE 40 min

SERVES 6

15 ml	**(1 Tbsp) olive oil**
▲ 2	**onions, chopped**
3	**garlic cloves, minced**
▲ 1	**bunch broccoli, stems chopped and tops cut into small florets**
▲ 175 ml	**(¾ cup) reduced-sodium vegetable broth**
0.5 ml	**(⅛ tsp) cayenne**
875 ml	**(3 ½ cups) water**
2 ml	**(½ tsp) salt**
▲ 250 ml	**(1 cup) yellow cornmeal**
75 ml	**(⅓ cup) grated Romano cheese**

1. Preheat oven to 190°C (375°F). Spray 25 cm (10-inch) pie plate or casserole dish with nonstick spray.

2. Heat oil in deep large nonstick skillet over medium heat. Add onions and cook, stirring, until golden, about 7 minutes. Add garlic and cook, stirring, until fragrant, about 30 seconds. Add broccoli, broth and cayenne; cook, stirring occasionally, until broccoli is tender and most of liquid is evaporated, about 10 minutes longer. Remove skillet from heat

3. Meanwhile, to make polenta, bring water and salt to boil in large nonstick saucepan. Reduce heat to medium; slowly whisk in cornmeal in thin, steady stream. Reduce heat to low and cook, stirring constantly with wooden spoon, until very thick, about 10 minutes. Pour polenta into prepared pie plate and spread evenly.

4. Spoon broccoli mixture over polenta; sprinkle with Romano. Bake until heated through and browned, about 20 minutes. Let stand 5 minutes before serving.

PER SERVING (⅙ OF CASSEROLE): 355 grams, 169 Cal, 4 g Total Fat, 1 g Sat Fat, 0 g Trans Fat, 2 mg Chol, 319 mg Sod, 29 g Total Carb, 6 g Total Sugar, 6 g Fib, 7 g Prot, 87 mg Calc.

 The **casserole** can be assembled up to several hours before baking and set aside at room temperature.

Winter Vegetable Casserole

LEVEL Basic
PREP 20 min
COOK 45 min
SERVES 6

15 ml	(1 Tbsp) olive oil
▲ 1	**large onion, chopped**
▲ 3	**carrots, cut into small dice**
▲ 3	**celery stalks, cut into small dice**
▲ 2	**parsnips, cut into small dice**
3	**garlic cloves, minced**
▲ 2	**475 ml (15 ½ fl oz) cans red kidney beans, rinsed and drained**
▲ 250 ml	**(1 cup) reduced-sodium vegetable broth**
5 ml	**(1 tsp) dried oregano**
3 ml	**(¾ tsp) salt**
2 ml	**(½ tsp) black pepper**
▲ 1 L	**(4 cups) hot cooked quinoa**

1. Heat oil in nonstick Dutch oven over medium heat. Add onion, carrots, celery, and parsnips; cook, stirring, until onion is golden, about 7 minutes. Add garlic and cook, stirring, until fragrant, about 30 seconds.

2. Stir in all remaining ingredients except quinoa; bring to boil. Reduce heat and simmer, covered, until vegetables are tender and flavours are blended, about 30 minutes. Serve over quinoa.

PER SERVING (375 ML [1 ½ CUPS] CASSEROLE AND 150 ML [²⁄₃ CUP] QUINOA): 326 grams, 337 Cal, 5 g Total Fat, 5 g Sat Fat, 0 g Trans Fat, 0 mg Chol, 572 mg Sod, 62 g Total Carb, 10 g Total Sugar, 12 g Fib, 14 g Prot, 118 mg Calc.

▲ **HEALTHY EXTRA** Begin the meal with a generous mixed greens, cucumber, and radicchio salad dressed with lemon juice.

Lentil-Bean Chili

8
PointsPlus®
value™

Per Serving

LEVEL Basic

PREP 15 min

COOK 45 min

SERVES 6

15 ml	(1 Tbsp) canola oil
▲ 1	large onion chopped
▲ 1	796 ml (28 fl oz) can crushed tomatoes
▲ 250 ml	(1 cup) reduced-sodium vegetable broth
▲ 375 ml	(1 ½ cups) lentils, picked over, rinsed, and drained
▲ 250 ml	(1 cup) fresh or frozen corn kernels
▲ 1	red bell pepper, diced
▲ 1	green bell pepper, diced
10 ml	(2 tsp) chili powder or to taste
10 ml	(2 tsp) ground cumin
2 ml	(½ tsp) salt
▲ 1	475 ml (15 ½ fl oz) can black beans, rinsed and drained
▲ 90 ml	(6 Tbsp) fat-free sour cream

1. Heat oil in nonstick Dutch oven over medium heat. Add onion and cook, stirring, until softened, about 5 minutes. Add tomatoes, broth, and lentils; bring to boil. Reduce heat and simmer, covered, 20 minutes.

2. Add corn, bell peppers, chili powder, cumin, and salt to pot. Return to boil. Reduce heat and simmer, covered, until lentils and vegetables are tender, about 15 minutes. Add beans and cook until heated through, about 2 minutes longer. Serve with sour cream.

PER SERVING (ABOUT 310 ML [1 ¼ CUPS] CHILI AND 15 ML [1 TBSP] SOUR CREAM): 487 grams, 344 Cal, 4 g Total Fat, 0 g Sat Fat, 0 g Trans Fat, 5 mg Chol, 630 mg Sod, 58 g Total Carb, 13 g Total Sugar, 18 g Fib, 21 g Prot, 165 mg Calc.

▲ **HEALTHY EXTRA** Make this chili even more delicious by topping it with chopped scallions and fresh cilantro.

Stir-Fried Tempeh and Vegetables with Barley

8 PointsPlus© value™ Per Serving

LEVEL Basic

PREP 20 min

COOK 10 min

SERVES 6

1	250 g (8 oz) package tempeh, cut into 0.5 cm (¼-inch) slices
▲ 250 ml	(1 cup) reduced-sodium vegetable broth
60 ml	(¼ cup) creamy peanut butter
45 ml	(3 Tbsp) reduced-sodium soy sauce
15 ml	(1 Tbsp) grated peeled fresh ginger
10 ml	(2 tsp) canola oil
▲ 250 g	(½ lb) shiitake mushrooms, stemmed and quartered
▲ 250 g	(½ lb) snow peas
▲ 1	yellow bell pepper, thinly sliced
▲ 6	scallions, cut into 5 cm (2 inch) lengths
▲ 750 ml	(3 cups) hot cooked pearl barley

1. Half-fill medium saucepan with water and bring to boil; add tempeh. Reduce heat and simmer until softened, about 5 minutes; drain.

2. Meanwhile, to make sauce, whisk together broth, peanut butter, soy sauce, and ginger in small bowl until blended.

3. Heat nonstick wok or deep large skillet over high heat until drop of water sizzles in pan; add oil and swirl to coat pan. Add mushrooms, snow peas, and bell pepper; stir-fry until bell pepper is crisp-tender, about 3 minutes. Add scallions and sauce; stir-fry until vegetables are coated with peanut sauce and scallions are softened, about 2 minutes longer. Serve with barley.

PER SERVING (⅙ OF TEMPEH MIXTURE AND 125 ML [½ CUP] BARLEY): 285 grams, 291 Cal, 12 g Total Fat, 2 g Sat Fat, 0 g Trans Fat, 0 mg Chol, 440 mg Sod, 36 g Total Carb, 5 g Total Sugar, 8 g Fib, 15 g Prot, 87 mg Calc.

FYI **Tempeh** is made from fermented soy bean curds. It has a firmer texture than tofu and a slightly nutty, smoky flavour. It is high in protein, cholesterol free, and very low in fat. It is available fresh and frozen. Tempeh can be refrigerated for up to 2 weeks and frozen for up to 3 months.

4

Light Meal or Snack

Beef and Parmesan Bruschetta

LEVEL Basic

PREP 15 min

COOK 10 min

SERVES 6

▲ 1   **250 g (8 oz) beef tenderloin, trimmed**

5 ml   **(1 tsp) olive oil**

1 ml   **(¼ tsp) salt**

1 ml   **(¼ tsp) black pepper**

▲ 125 ml **(½ cup) lightly packed mixed baby salad greens**

1   **250 g (8 oz) piece whole grain Italian bread, cut into 12 slices and toasted**

5 ml   **(1 tsp) white truffle oil or extra-virgin olive oil**

1   **30 g (1 oz) piece Parmesan cheese, made into shavings with vegetable peeler**

1. Heat large nonstick skillet over medium-high heat. Rub tenderloin with olive oil, salt, and pepper. Place in skillet and cook until browned on all sides and instant-read thermometer inserted into centre of beef registers 60°C (140°F) for medium, about 8 minutes. Transfer to cutting board and let stand 5 minutes. Thinly slice across grain.

2. Divide salad greens evenly among toasts; top evenly with beef. Drizzle evenly with truffle oil and top with Parmesan shavings.

PER SERVING (2 BRUSCHETTA): 72 grams, 182 Cal, 6 g Total Fat, 2 g Sat Fat, 1 g Trans Fat, 22 mg Chol, 418 mg Sod, 21 g Total Carb, 2 g Total Sugar, 2 g Fib, 12 g Prot, 74 mg Calc.

FYI **Truffle oil** adds an unexpected rich and exotic flavour to these bruschetta. It is found online and in specialty food stores.

Korean-Style Barbecue Beef

LEVEL Basic
PREP 15 min
BROIL 5 min
SERVES 8

125 ml	**(½ cup) unseasoned rice vinegar**
60 ml	**(¼ cup) reduced-sodium soy sauce**
▲ 1	**small onion, finely chopped**
2	**garlic cloves, minced**
30 ml	**(2 Tbsp) brown sugar**
15 ml	**(1 Tbsp) grated peeled fresh ginger**
10 ml	**(2 tsp) fish sauce**
5 ml	**(1 tsp) chili garlic sauce**
▲ 625 g	**(1 ¼ lb) flank steak, trimmed and cut into thin strips**
10 ml	**(2 tsp) sesame seeds, toasted**

1. Soak 16 (30 cm [12 inch]) wooden skewers in water at least 30 minutes.

2. Meanwhile, to make marinade, combine all ingredients except flank steak and sesame seeds in small bowl.

3. Thread beef evenly onto skewers; place in large baking dish. Pour marinade over beef. Cover and refrigerate, turning skewers occasionally, at least 2 hours or up to 5 hours.

4. Spray broiler rack with nonstick spray. Preheat broiler.

5. Place skewers on broiler rack. Broil 10 cm (4 inches) from heat until beef is browned, about 3 minutes per side. Sprinkle with sesame seeds.

PER SERVING (2 SKEWERS): 79 grams, 128 Cal, 6 g Total Fat, 2 g Sat Fat, 0 g Trans Fat, 30 mg Chol, 477 mg Sod, 5 g Total Carb, 4 g Total Sugar, 0 g Fib, 13 g Prot, 9 mg Calc.

▲ **HEALTHY EXTRA** Serve with a quickly tossed salad of broccoli slaw mix, lemon juice and a pinch of salt and black pepper.

Pork and Scallion Roll-Ups

Pork and Scallion Roll-Ups

3 PointsPlus value
Per Serving

LEVEL Basic
PREP 15 min
BROIL 5 min
SERVES 6

▲ 1   **375 g (¾ lb) lean pork tenderloin, trimmed and cut into 18 slices**

15 ml   **(1 Tbsp) reduced-sodium soy sauce**

15 ml   **(1 Tbsp) oyster sauce**

15 ml   **(1 Tbsp) honey**

15 ml   **(1 Tbsp) Asian (dark) sesame oil**

10 ml   **(2 tsp) grated peeled fresh ginger**

▲ 18   **scallions, cut into 7.5 cm (3 inch) lengths**

1. Place slices of pork between two pieces of plastic wrap. With meat mallet or rolling pin, slightly flatten each slice.

2. To make marinade, stir together soy sauce, oyster sauce, honey, sesame oil, and ginger in large bowl. Add pork and toss to coat. Let stand about 20 minutes.

3. Preheat broiler. Line rack of broiler pan with foil.

4. Wrap 1 slice of pork around each scallion length. Arrange rolls, seam side down, on prepared broiler rack. Broil 12.5 cm (5 inches) from heat until pork is browned and scallions are just tender, about 5 minutes.

PER SERVING (3 ROLLS): 67 grams, 104 Cal, 4 g Total Fat, 1 g Sat Fat, 0 g Trans Fat, 32 mg Chol, 144 mg Sod, 5 g Total Carb, 3 g Total Sugar, 1 g Fib, 12 g Prot, 15 mg Calc.

 FYI For a more intense flavour, **marinate the pork** in the refrigerator for up to 2 hours.

Shrimp Cakes with Tarragon Mayonnaise

LEVEL Intermediate

PREP 30 min

COOK 20 min

SERVES 14

▲ **500 g** **(1 lb) cooked shrimp, chopped**

175 ml **(¾ cup) plain dried bread crumbs**

125 ml **(½ cup) fat-free mayonnaise**

▲ **2** **scallions, finely chopped**

20 ml **(4 tsp) Dijon mustard**

▲ **1** **large egg white**

▲ **60 ml** **(¼ cup) finely chopped unsweetened pickle**

15 ml **(1 Tbsp) chopped fresh tarragon**

15 ml **(1 Tbsp) canola oil**

1. To make shrimp cakes, stir together shrimp, 60 ml (¼ cup) of bread crumbs, 60 ml (¼ cup) of mayonnaise, the scallions, 15 ml (3 tsp) of mustard, and the egg white in large bowl. With damp hands, shape mixture into 14 patties.

2. Put remaining 125 ml (½ cup) bread crumbs on sheet of wax paper. Coat patties in crumbs, then transfer to wax paper–lined plate. Cover with plastic wrap and refrigerate until firm, at least 30 minutes or up to 4 hours.

3. Meanwhile, to make tarragon mayonnaise, stir together remaining 60 ml (¼ cup) mayonnaise, the pickle, tarragon, and remaining 5 ml (1 tsp) mustard in serving bowl.

4. Heat oil in large nonstick skillet over medium-high heat. Cook patties, in batches, until crisp and golden, about 3 minutes per side. Serve with tarragon mayonnaise.

PER SERVING (1 SHRIMP CAKE AND 10 ML [2 TSP] MAYONNAISE): 57 grams, 75 Cal, 2 g Total Fat, 0 g Sat Fat, 0 g Trans Fat, 64 mg Chol, 259 mg Sod, 6 g Total Carb, 1 g Total Sugar, 1 g Fib, 8 g Prot, 26 mg Calc.

▲ **HEALTHY EXTRA** Serve these delectable shrimp cakes on a bed of your favourite salad greens accompanied by thick slices of tomato and sweet onion drizzled with balsamic vinegar.

Chicken Satay
with Spicy Peanut Sauce

LEVEL Basic

PREP 20 min

BROIL 10 min

SERVES 8

45 ml	**(3 Tbsp) creamy peanut butter**
10 ml	**(2 tsp) sugar**
2	**garlic cloves, minced**
30 ml	**(2 Tbsp) reduced-sodium soy sauce**
15 ml	**(1 Tbsp) water**
10 ml	**(2 tsp) red wine vinegar**
Several	**drops Sriracha (hot chili sauce)**
▲ 2	**150 g (5 oz) skinless boneless chicken breasts, each cut into 6 lengthwise strips**

1. Soak (30 cm [12 inch]) wooden skewers in water at least 30 minutes. Line rack of broiler pan with foil and spray with nonstick spray.

2. To make sauce, whisk together peanut butter, sugar, and garlic in small bowl until blended. Add soy sauce, water, vinegar, and Sriracha, whisking until blended. Transfer to serving bowl.

3. Preheat broiler.

4. Thread chicken onto skewers and spray with nonstick spray. Place skewers on rack of broiler pan. Broil 12.5 cm (5 inches) from heat until cooked through, about 4 minutes per side. Serve with peanut sauce.

PER SERVING (1 SKEWER AND ABOUT 15 ML [1 TBSP] SAUCE): 39 grams, 81 Cal, 4 g Total Fat, 1 g Sat Fat, 0 g Trans Fat, 20 mg Chol, 200 mg Sod, 3 g Total Carb, 2 g Total Sugar, 0 g Fib, 9 g Prot, 7 mg Calc.

Green Curry Seafood

3
PointsPlus®
value™

Per Serving

LEVEL Basic

PREP 20 min

COOK 10 min

SERVES 8

15 ml	(1 Tbsp) canola oil
3	shallots, minced
15 ml	(1 Tbsp) grated peeled fresh ginger
15 ml	(1 Tbsp) brown sugar
15 ml	(1 Tbsp) Asian fish sauce
5 ml	(1 tsp) Thai green curry paste
1	400 ml (14 fl oz) can light (low-fat) coconut milk
▲ 1 kg	(2 lb) littleneck clams, scrubbed
▲ 750 g	(1 ½ lb) peeled and deveined large shrimp
125 ml	(½ cup) coarsely chopped fresh basil

1. Heat oil in large nonstick Dutch oven over low heat. Add shallots, ginger, brown sugar, fish sauce, and curry paste. Cook, stirring constantly, until fragrant, about 1 minute.

2. Stir coconut milk and clams into pot; increase heat and bring to simmer. Cook, covered, until clams begin to open, about 5 minutes. Stir in shrimp. Cover and cook until clams have opened and shrimp are just opaque in centre, about 4 minutes. Discard any clams that do not open. Serve sprinkled with basil.

PER SERVING (ABOUT 500 ML [2 CUPS]): 132 grams, 123 Cal, 5 g Total Fat, 0 g Sat Fat, 0 g Trans Fat, 132 mg Chol, 223 mg Sod, 5 g Total Carb, 1 g Total Sugar, 0 g Fib, 16 g Prot, 39 mg Calc.

▲ **HEALTHY EXTRA** Serve this bold-flavoured Thai dish over brown basmati rice (150 ml [2/3 cup] of cooked brown basmati rice with each serving will increase the *PointsPlus* value by *3*).

Green Curry Seafood

Liquids

▶ **Start your meal with a bowl of broth.** Besides being a great way to sneak in extra liquids, research suggests that having a broth-based soup as a first course can lead you to consume fewer calories during the rest of the meal.

▶ **Munch on water-rich produce.** Fruits and vegetables have a naturally high water content, so by noshing on grapes, watermelon, tomatoes, cucumber, celery, and bell pepper wedges, you'll boost your water intake.

▶ **Don't rely on thirst.** Thirst is a poor indicator of your hydration status; in fact, some experts say you're already somewhat dehydrated by the time your thirst mechanism kicks in. So it's best to consume fluids regularly throughout the day—before you feel thirsty.

Food Processor White Bean and Tomatillo Dip

2 PointsPlus® value™
Per Serving

LEVEL Basic

PREP 15 min

COOK None

SERVES 6

▲ **2** 475 ml (15½-ounce) cans small white beans, rinsed and drained

▲ **1** 375 ml (12-ounce) can tomatillos, drained and coarsely chopped

▲ **1** 135 ml (4½-ounce) can chopped mild green chiles, drained

▲ **½** small red onion, finely chopped

125 ml (½ cup) chopped fresh cilantro

45 ml (3 Tbsp) lime juice

10 ml (2 tsp) chili powder

1 ml (¼ tsp) salt

4 drops hot pepper sauce or to taste

Combine beans and tomatillos in food processor and pulse until chunky purée forms. Transfer bean mixture to serving bowl and stir in remaining ingredients.

PER SERVING (75 ML [⅓ CUP]): 160 grams, 94 Cal, 1 g Total Fat, 0 g Sat Fat, 0 g Trans Fat, 0 mg Chol, 321 mg Sod, 16 g Total Carb, 1 g Total Sugar, 5 g Fib, 4 g Prot, 34 mg Calc.

▲ **HEALTHY EXTRA** Serve this unusual dip surrounded by Belgian endive leaves.

Chunky Guacamole

Chunky Guacamole

1 PointsPlus® value ™ Per Serving

LEVEL Basic
PREP 15 min
COOK None
SERVES 16

2	**ripe avocados, halved, pitted, and peeled**
▲ **1**	**small jalapeño pepper, seeded and minced**
▲ **½**	**small red onion, chopped**
125 ml	**(½ cup) chopped fresh cilantro**
15 ml	**(1 Tbsp) lime juice**
2 ml	**(½ tsp) salt**
▲ **1 L**	**(4 cups) vegetables, such as halved baby carrots or radishes, asparagus lengths, celery sticks, and cherry tomatoes**

Coarsely mash avocados in serving bowl. Add all remaining ingredients except cut-up vegetables, stirring until mixed well. Serve at once or press a piece of plastic wrap directly onto surface to prevent guacamole from browning. Serve with cut-up vegetables. Can be refrigerated up to 2 hours.

PER SERVING (30 ML [2 TBSP]): 57 grams, 45 Cal, 3 g Total Fat, 1 g Sat Fat, 0 g Trans Fat, 0 mg Chol, 79 mg Sod, 4 g Total Carb, 1 g Total Sugar, 3 g Fib, 1 g Prot, 7 mg Calc.

FYI There are two types of avocados: Hass and Florida (Fuerte). Hass avocados have a dark green pebbly texture that turns almost black when ripe and a rich buttery taste. Florida avocados are much larger with bright green smooth skin and a less intense flavour.

Ricotta, Parmesan, and Sun-Dried Tomato Dip

LEVEL Basic

PREP 10 min

COOK None

SERVES 8

Stir together all ingredients except baguette in serving bowl. Serve with toasts.

▲ 1   **450 g (15 oz) container fat-free ricotta cheese**

60 ml   **(¼ cup) fat-free mayonnaise**

▲ 60 ml   **(¼ cup) moist-packed sun-dried tomatoes (not packed in oil), finely chopped**

60 ml   **(¼ cup) chopped fresh basil**

30 ml   **(2 Tbsp) grated Parmesan cheese**

Pinch cayenne

1   **250 g (8 oz) piece whole grain French baguette, cut into 16 slices and toasted**

PER SERVING (60 ML [¼ CUP] DIP AND 2 TOASTS):
94 grams, 135 Cal, 1 g Total Fat, 0 g Sat Fat, 0 g Trans Fat, 10 mg Chol, 347 mg Sod, 22 g Total Carb, 4 g Total Sugar, 2 g Fib, 8 g Prot, 118 mg Calc.

FYI There are three types of **sun-dried tomatoes** available: moist packed, packed in oil, and dry (which have to be soaked to soften). Moist-packed sun-dried tomatoes are sold in airtight plastic bags, which keep them moist and fresh. They do not contain any oil, which keeps calories low.

Jalapeño Hummus

LEVEL Basic

PREP 5 min

COOK None

SERVES 4

▲ 1   **475 ml (15 ½ fl oz) can chickpeas, rinsed and drained**

30 ml   **(2 Tbsp) tahini**

▲ ½-1   **jalapeño pepper, seeded and minced**

30 ml   **(2 Tbsp) lime juice**

30 ml   **(2 Tbsp) water**

1   **garlic clove, minced**

1 ml   **(¼ tsp) salt**

30 ml   **(2 Tbsp) chopped fresh cilantro**

Combine all ingredients except cilantro in food processor and pulse until smooth, adding a little water if hummus is too stiff. Transfer to serving bowl and sprinkle with cilantro.

PER SERVING (60 ML [¼ CUP]): 97 grams, 110 Cal, 5 g Total Fat, 1 g Sat Fat, 0 g Trans Fat, 0 mg Chol, 362 mg Sod, 13 g Total Carb, 1 g Total Sugar, 3 g Fib, 5 g Prot, 36 mg Calc.

▲ **HEALTHY EXTRA** Serve this hummus accompanied by dippers, such as broccoli florets, zucchini slices, thickly sliced large white mushrooms, and whole radishes with their leaves attached.

Fruits & Vegetables

▶ **Consume a rainbow a day.** To meet (or exceed) your daily quota of fruits and veggies and to maximize the nutritional benefits from your choices, choose a different colour with each selection: red (red bell peppers, tomatoes, apples), orange (carrots, oranges, cantaloupe), yellow (summer squash, corn, peaches), green (spinach, kale, broccoli, grapes), blue or purple (eggplant, red cabbage, blueberries, grapes), white (onions, leeks, turnips, honeydew melon), and so on.

▶ **Snack on veggies.** Carrot, celery, and zucchini sticks are excellent (nutrient- and fibre-rich) finger foods to munch on between meals. Prepare a batch ahead of time and keep them in the fridge to snack on when the urge strikes.

▶ **Put out a fruit bowl.** Whether you set the bowl on your kitchen table or on the counter, having fresh fruit—apples, bananas, oranges, pears—within easy reach will encourage everyone in your family to grab a healthy snack. This strategy is the opposite of out of sight, out of mind: By keeping healthy choices in your field of vision, you'll be more likely to gravitate toward them.

Classic Devilled Eggs

3 PointsPlus value ™ Per Serving

LEVEL Basic

PREP 15 min

COOK 5 min

SERVES 6

▲ **6**	**large eggs**
45 ml	**(3 Tbsp) fat-free mayonnaise**
2 ml	**(½ tsp) mustard powder**
2 ml	**(½ tsp) white wine vinegar**
1 ml	**(¼ tsp) black pepper**
0.5 ml	**(⅛ tsp) salt**
Paprika	

1. Place eggs in medium saucepan with enough water to cover by at least 2.5 cm (1 inch); bring to boil. Immediately remove saucepan from heat. Let stand, covered, 15 minutes. Pour off water; rinse eggs under cold running water to cool.

2. Peel eggs; cut lengthwise in half and remove yolks. Transfer yolks to small bowl and mash with fork until smooth. Add all remaining ingredients except paprika, stirring to mix well.

3. Place egg whites on platter. Spoon yolk mixture evenly into egg white halves or spoon yolk mixture into pastry bag fitted with star tip and pipe into egg white halves. Sprinkle with paprika and serve at once or loosely cover and refrigerate up to 4 hours.

PER SERVING (2 DEVILLED EGGS): 58 grams, 85 Cal, 6 g Total Fat, 2 g Sat Fat, 0 g Trans Fat, 213 mg Chol, 171 mg Sod, 2 g Total Carb, 1 g Total Sugar, 0 g Fib, 6 g Prot, 27 mg Calc.

▲ **HEALTHY EXTRA** Stir 15 ml (1 Tbsp) each of finely chopped celery, red bell pepper, and red onion into the yolk mixture in step 2.

Crab Salad–Topped Cucumber

PointsPlus© value

Per Serving

LEVEL Basic

PREP 20 min

COOK None

SERVES 4

▲ **125 g** **(¼ lb) lump crabmeat, picked over**

30 ml **(2 Tbsp) reduced-fat mayonnaise**

▲ **15 ml** **(1 Tbsp) finely chopped celery**

15 ml **(1 Tbsp) finely chopped chives**

10 ml **(2 tsp) lime juice**

Pinch cayenne

▲ **20** **thick cucumber slices**

Combine all ingredients except cucumber in medium bowl. Spoon about 5 ml (1 tsp) of crab mixture onto each cucumber slice. Arrange on platter and serve at once or cover and refrigerate up to 2 hours.

PER SERVING (5 CRAB-TOPPED CUCUMBER SLICES): 76 grams, 51 Cal, 5 g Total Fat, 0 g Sat Fat, 0 g Trans Fat, 19 mg Chol, 222 mg Sod, 2 g Total Carb, 0 g Total Sugar, 0 g Fib, 4 g Prot, 99 mg Calc.

FYI **Blue crabs**, found along the eastern seaboard and Gulf coast, are prized for their lump crabmeat. These succulent chunks of crab, which are taken from the body, are appreciated for their taste and texture. Be sure to buy crabmeat from a fish store with a good turnover, and pick it over for pieces of shell and cartilage.

Crab Salad-Topped Cucumber

Black Bean and Mushroom Quesadillas

LEVEL Basic
PREP 15 min
COOK 10 min
SERVES 6

▲ **170 g** **(6 oz) white mushrooms, sliced**

▲ **250 ml** **(1 cup) rinsed and drained canned black beans**

▲ **1** **small tomato, chopped**

▲ **2** **scallions, thinly sliced**

125 ml **(½ cup) shredded reduced-fat pepper Jack cheese**

4 **17 cm (7 inch) fat-free whole wheat tortillas**

▲ **75 ml** **(⅓ cup) fat-free sour cream**

1. Spray large nonstick skillet with nonstick spray and set over medium heat. Add mushrooms and cook, stirring, until mushrooms release their juice and it is evaporated, about 8 minutes. Transfer to plate and let cool slightly. Wipe skillet clean.

2. Layer one-fourth each of mushrooms, beans, tomato, scallions, and pepper Jack on half of each tortilla. Fold unfilled half of each tortilla over filling, pressing down lightly.

3. Spray skillet with nonstick spray and set over medium-high heat. Place 2 quesadillas in skillet and cook until browned in spots, about 3 minutes. Spray quesadillas with nonstick spray and turn over. Cook until quesadillas are browned in spots and filling is heated through, about 2 minutes longer. Transfer to cutting board; keep warm. Repeat with remaining 2 quesadillas. Cut each quesadilla into 3 wedges and serve with sour cream.

PER SERVING (2 WEDGES AND SCANT 15 ML [1 TBSP] SOUR CREAM): 148 grams, 155 Cal, 4 g Total Fat, 1 g Sat Fat, 0 g Trans Fat, 7 mg Chol, 267 mg Sod, 25 g Total Carb, 2 g Total Sugar, 4 g Fib, 8 g Prot, 165 mg Calc.

▲ **HEALTHY EXTRA** Accompany these tempting quesadillas with fat-free tomato or tomatillo salsa.

New York Deli–Style Quesadillas

LEVEL Basic

PREP 15 min

COOK 10 min

SERVES 4

60 ml	**(¼ cup) fat-free Thousand Island dressing**
2	**17 cm (7 inch) fat-free whole wheat tortillas**
▲ **1**	**125 g (¼ lb) piece skinless roasted turkey breast, shredded**
▲ **250 ml**	**(1 cup) tightly packed coleslaw mix**
125 ml	**(½ cup) shredded reduced-fat low-sodium Swiss cheese**

1. Spread dressing evenly over half of each tortilla. Layer one-fourth each of turkey, coleslaw, and Swiss over dressing. Fold unfilled half of each tortilla over filling, pressing down lightly.

2. Spray large skillet with nonstick spray and set over medium-high heat. Place 2 quesadillas in skillet and cook until browned in spots, about 3 minutes. Spray quesadillas with nonstick spray and turn over. Cook until bottoms of quesadillas are browned in spots and filling is heated through, about 2 minutes longer. Transfer to cutting board; keep warm. Repeat with remaining quesadillas. Cut each quesadilla in half.

PER SERVING (2 WEDGES): 101 grams, 159 Cal, 5 g Total Fat, 2 g Sat Fat, 0 g Trans Fat, 25 mg Chol, 244 mg Sod, 17 g Total Carb, 4 g Total Sugar, 2 g Fib, 12 g Prot, 182 mg Calc.

▲ **HEALTHY EXTRA** Serve spears of unsweetened pickles alongside the quesadillas for an authentic deli experience.

Provençal Tomato Tart

Provençal Tomato Tart

2
PointsPlus⊕
value
Per Serving

LEVEL Intermediate
PREP 20 min
BAKE 20 min
SERVES 12

▲ **5**   **large plum tomatoes, thinly sliced**

▲ **1**   **onion, very thinly sliced**

12   **pitted Kalamata olives, quartered**

10 ml   **(2 tsp) Herbes de Provence**

8   **30 cm x 43 cm (12 x 17 inch) sheets frozen phyllo dough, thawed**

125 ml   **(½ cup) grated Parmesan cheese**

1. Place tomato slices between sheets of paper towels and pat dry. Let stand 10 minutes. Mix together onion, olives, and Herbes de Provence in small bowl.

2. Preheat oven to 200°C (400°F). Spray baking sheet with nonstick spray.

3. Lay 1 sheet of phyllo on baking sheet; lightly spray with olive oil nonstick spray. (Keep remaining phyllo covered with damp paper towel and plastic wrap to keep it from drying out.). Repeat layering with remaining phyllo, spraying each sheet with nonstick spray. Roll edges of phyllo in to form rim.

4. Arrange tomato slices on phyllo in single layer; top with onion mixture. Lightly spray with nonstick spray. Bake until edges of phyllo are golden brown and tomatoes and onion are softened, about 20 minutes. Sprinkle with Parmesan. Cut tart into 12 equal pieces. Serve hot, warm, or at room temperature.

PER SERVING (1 PIECE): 54 grams, 64 Cal, 2 g Total Fat, 1 g Sat Fat, 0 g Trans Fat, 3 mg Chol, 199 mg Sod, 9 g Total Carb, 1 g Total Sugar, 1 g Fib, 3 g Prot, 55 mg Calc.

FYI   **Herbes de Provence** are a mix of dried herbs that are grown in the south of France. Packed into decorative red clay crocks, they are available in some supermarkets and in specialty food stores. Herbes de Provence usually includes basil, fennel, lavender, marjoram, rosemary, sage, and thyme. It is a very fragrant blend, so a little goes a long way.

Caramelized Onion-Feta Squares

LEVEL Intermediate

PREP 15 min

COOK/BAKE 45 min

SERVES 12

10 ml	**(2 tsp) olive oil**
▲ 3	**onions, thinly sliced**
5 ml	**(1 tsp) sugar**
2 ml	**(½ tsp) salt**
1 ml	**(¼ tsp) black pepper**
1	**500 g (16 oz) refrigerated whole wheat pizza dough, at room temperature**
125 g	**(4 oz) reduced-fat feta cheese, crumbled**
5 ml	**(1 tsp) dried thyme**

1. Heat oil in large nonstick skillet over low heat. Add onions; sprinkle with sugar, salt, and pepper. Cook, stirring, until onions are softened and golden brown, about 25 minutes, adding a little water if onions seem dry. Remove skillet from heat; let cool slightly.

2. Set rack on lowest rung of oven. Preheat oven to 230°C (450°F). Spray 27 x 39 cm (10 ½ x 15 ½ inch) jelly-roll pan with olive oil nonstick spray.

3. With floured hands, stretch and press pizza dough into prepared pan. Spread onion mixture over dough; sprinkle with feta and thyme.

4. Bake until crust is nicely browned and cheese is softened, about 20 minutes. Cut into 12 equal pieces.

PER SERVING (1 PIECE): 78 grams, 126 Cal, 3 g Total Fat, 1 g Sat Fat, 0 g Trans Fat, 3 mg Chol, 221 mg Sod, 20 g Total Carb, 2 g Total Sugar, 3 g Fib, 5 g Prot, 39 mg Calc.

FYI To make the **pizza dough** easier to work with, allow it to stand (covered) at room temperature for about 15 minutes. This short resting time will enable the dough to relax, making it easier to stretch in the pan.

Oven-Roasted Eggplant–Bell Pepper Bruschetta

LEVEL Basic

PREP 15 min

ROAST 45 min

SERVES 12

▲ 1   **500 g (1 lb) eggplant, cut into 1.25 cm (½ inch) pieces**

▲ 2   **red bell peppers, chopped**

▲ 2   **zucchini, thinly sliced**

15 ml   **(1 Tbsp) extra-virgin olive oil**

2 ml   **(½ tsp) salt**

1 ml   **(¼ tsp) black pepper**

1   **250 g (8 oz) piece French baguette, cut into 24 slices and toasted**

60 ml   **(¼ cup) lightly packed thinly sliced fresh basil**

30 ml   **(2 Tbsp) grated Romano cheese**

1. Preheat oven to 220°C (425°F).

2. Toss together eggplant, bell peppers, zucchini, oil, salt, and black pepper in large shallow roasting pan. Spread to form single layer. Roast, stirring occasionally, until vegetables are tender and lightly browned, about 45 minutes.

3. Spoon vegetable mixture evenly onto toasts. Sprinkle evenly with basil and Romano.

PER SERVING (2 BRUSCHETTA): 110 grams, 115 Cal, 4 g Total Fat, 1 g Sat Fat, 0 g Trans Fat, 1 mg Chol, 226 mg Sod, 19 g Total Carb, 3 g Total Sugar, 3 g Fib, 3 g Prot, 26 mg Calc.

FYI **Romano cheese**, which gets its name from the city of Rome, is a sharp-tasting, tangy cheese. The best-known type of Romano is Pecorino-Romano, which is made from sheep's milk.

Escarole Salad Pizza

4 PointsPlus© value ™
Per Serving

LEVEL Basic
PREP 20 min
BAKE 10 min
SERVES 6

1	**290 g (10 oz) prebaked thin whole wheat pizza crust**
30 ml	**(2 Tbsp) grated Parmesan cheese**
30 ml	**(2 Tbsp) red wine vinegar**
15 ml	**(1 Tbsp) extra-virgin olive oil**
2 ml	**(½ tsp) dried oregano**
1 ml	**(¼ tsp) black pepper**
▲ 500 ml	**(2 cups) lightly packed thinly sliced escarole**
▲ 250 ml	**(1 cup) lightly packed thinly sliced radicchio**
▲ 1	**small red bell pepper, thinly sliced**
▲ 1	**small red onion, thinly sliced**
▲ 2	**plum tomatoes, chopped**
▲ 4	**moist-packed sun-dried tomatoes (not packed in oil), chopped**

1. Preheat oven to 200°C (400°F).

2. Place pizza crust directly on oven rack; bake until crispy, about 10 minutes.

3. Meanwhile, to make dressing, whisk together Parmesan, vinegar, oil, oregano, and black pepper in large bowl. Add remaining ingredients to dressing; toss to coat evenly. Spoon onto pizza crust. Cut into 6 wedges.

PER SERVING (1 WEDGE): 119 grams, 171 Cal, 5 g Total Fat, 2 g Sat Fat, 0 g Trans Fat, 1 mg Chol, 299 mg Sod, 27 g Total Carb, 3 g Total Sugar, 6 g Fib, 7 g Prot, 90 mg Calc.

Escarole Salad Pizza

Chickpea–Goat Cheese Toasts

LEVEL Basic
PREP 15 min
ROAST 20 min
SERVES 6

▲ 1   **475 ml (15 ½ fl oz) can chickpeas, rinsed and drained**

2   **garlic cloves, minced**

5 ml   **(1 tsp) ground cumin**

5 ml   **(1 tsp) olive oil**

▲ 1   **tomato, chopped**

1 ml   **(¼ tsp) salt**

0.5 ml   **(⅛ tsp) black pepper**

3   **15 cm (6 inch) whole wheat pita breads, each cut into 4 wedges**

30 g   **(1 oz) soft goat cheese, crumbled**

1. Preheat oven to 200°C (400°F).

2. Mix together chickpeas, garlic, cumin, and oil in 20 cm (8 inch) square baking dish. Roast, stirring occasionally, 15 minutes. Transfer chickpeas to medium bowl; stir in tomato, salt, and pepper.

3. Arrange pita bread wedges on baking sheet. Bake until crisp, about 5 minutes.

4. Spoon chickpea mixture evenly onto pita wedges; sprinkle evenly with goat cheese. Serve warm.

PER SERVING (2 TOASTS): 111 grams, 154 Cal, 3 g Total Fat, 1 g Sat Fat, 0 g Trans Fat, 2 mg Chol, 430 mg Sod, 26 g Total Carb, 2 g Total Sugar, 5 g Fib, 7 g Prot, 33 mg Calc.

FYI   **Mash chickpeas slightly** after baking to help prevent them from rolling off the toasted pita wedges.

Nachos Pizzeria Style

3 PointsPlus® value
Per Serving

LEVEL Basic

PREP 15 min

BROIL 1 min

SERVES 4

24	**baked tortilla chips**
125 ml	**(½ cup) fat-free marinara sauce**
▲ 24	**slices white mushrooms**
125 ml	**(½ cup) shredded part-skim mozzarella cheese**
2 ml	**(½ tsp) dried oregano**
2 ml	**(½ tsp) dried basil**

1. Preheat broiler.

2. Place tortilla chips in jelly-roll pan in single layer. Spoon 5 ml (1 tsp) marinara sauce on each chip; top each with mushroom slice and 5 ml (1 tsp) mozzarella. Sprinkle evenly with oregano and basil. Broil until cheese begins to melt, about 1 minute.

PER SERVING (6 NACHOS): 59 grams, 108 Cal, 3 g Total Fat, 2 g Sat Fat, 0 g Trans Fat, 8 mg Chol, 221 mg Sod, 15 g Total Carb, 3 g Total Sugar, 2 g Fib, 5 g Prot, 137 mg Calc.

▲ **HEALTHY EXTRA** Top each nacho with one or two thin zucchini slices along with the mushrooms.

Curried Fruit and Nut Popcorn
and Nachos Pizzeria Style, page 157

Curried Fruit and Nut Popcorn

2 PointsPlus value
TM
Per Serving

LEVEL Basic

PREP 5 min

MICROWAVE 1 min

SERVES 8

15 ml	**(1 Tbsp) olive oil**
10 ml	**(2 tsp) curry powder**
▲ 1.5 L	**(6 cups) plain air-popped popcorn**
125 ml	**(½ cup) finely chopped dried apricots**
75 ml	**(⅓ cup) pistachio nuts, chopped**

1. Stir together oil and curry powder in microwavable cup. Microwave on High until fragrant, about 1 minute.

2. Toss together remaining ingredients in large bowl. Drizzle curry oil over popcorn and toss to coat evenly.

PER SERVING (175 ML [¾ CUP]): 29 grams, 83 Cal, 5 g Total Fat, 1 g Sat Fat, 0 g Trans Fat, 0 mg Chol, 22 mg Sod, 10 g Total Carb, 3 g Total Sugar, 2 g Fib, 2 g Prot, 11 mg Calc.

Spicy Garlic and Onion Pita Chips

PointsPlus⊕ value
Per Serving

LEVEL Basic
PREP 15 min
BAKE 10 min
SERVES 8

4	**15 cm (6 inch) oat bran pita breads**
▲ 2	**large egg whites**
3	**garlic cloves, minced**
5 ml	**(1 tsp) onion powder**
1 ml	**(¼ tsp) salt**
1 ml	**(¼ tsp) cayenne or to taste**
45 ml	**(3 Tbsp) grated Parmesan cheese**

1. Preheat oven to 180°C (350°F).

2. Split each pita in half to make 8 rounds total; cut each round into 6 wedges. Arrange wedges, smooth side down, on one or two baking sheets.

3. Beat egg whites, garlic, onion powder, salt, and cayenne in small bowl until frothy. Brush over pita wedges; sprinkle evenly with Parmesan.

4. Bake until edges of pita chips are browned and topping is set, about 10 minutes. Transfer chips to racks and let cool completely.

PER SERVING (6 CHIPS): 30 grams, 46 Cal, 2 g Total Fat, 0 g Sat Fat, 0 g Trans Fat, 2 mg Chol, 272 mg Sod, 5 g Total Carb, 0 g Total Sugar, 2 g Fib, 5 g Prot, 29 mg Calc.

FYI These tasty pita chips can be stored in an airtight container for up to 5 days.

Sugar and Spice Popcorn

LEVEL Basic

PREP 10 min

COOK None

SERVES 8

▲ **2 L** **(8 cups) plain air-popped popcorn**

30 ml **(2 Tbsp) superfine sugar**

10 ml **(2 tsp) ground cinnamon**

1 ml **(¼ tsp) ground allspice**

1 ml **(¼ tsp) ground cloves**

1 ml **(¼ tsp) ground ginger**

1 ml **(¼ tsp) ground nutmeg**

1. Put popcorn in very large bowl. Lightly spray with nonstick spray, tossing constantly while spraying.

2. Mix together remaining ingredients in cup. Gradually sprinkle over popcorn, tossing to coat evenly.

PER SERVING (250 ML [1 CUP]): 96 grams, 45 Cal, 0 g Total Fat, 0 g Sat Fat, 0 g Trans Fat, 0 mg Chol, 1 mg Sod, 10 g Total Carb, 3 g Total Sugar, 2 g Fib, 1 g Prot, 9 mg Calc.

FYI Here's how to **turn regular sugar into superfine sugar:** Put the sugar into a blender or food processor and process until fine. It's quick and costs less than store-bought superfine sugar.

Mini Banana-Walnut Parfaits

LEVEL Basic

PREP 15 min

COOK None

SERVES 4

4	vanilla wafer cookies, coarsely crushed
250 ml	(1 cup) chocolate fat-free frozen yogourt
30 ml	(2 Tbsp) chopped walnuts
▲ 1	small banana, cut into 12 slices
30 ml	(2 Tbsp) fat-free hot fudge topping
▲ 4	small strawberries with stems

Layer one-fourth of cookies, frozen yogourt, walnuts, banana, and fudge topping in each of 4 small wine glasses. Top each with 1 strawberry.

PER SERVING (1 PARFAIT): 87 grams, 136 Cal, 4 g Total Fat, 1 g Sat Fat, 0 g Trans Fat, 1 mg Chol, 61 mg Sod, 25 g Total Carb, 17 g Total Sugar, 2 g Fib, 4 g Prot, 99 mg Calc.

FYI If you have the time, **toast the walnuts**, as it brings out their nutty flavour and crisps them. Here's how: Place the nuts in a small dry skillet over medium-low heat. Cook, shaking the pan often, until the nuts are lightly browned and fragrant, about 4 minutes. Transfer to a plate to cool.

Chocolate-Orange Mousse

LEVEL Intermediate

PREP 5 min

COOK 10 min

SERVES 8

125 g	**(4 oz) semisweet chocolate, chopped**
22 ml	**(1 ½ Tbsp) orange liqueur**
15 ml	**(1 Tbsp) light corn syrup**
75 ml	**(⅓ cup) warm water**
▲ **30 ml**	**(2 Tbsp) powdered egg whites**
60 ml	**(¼ cup) sugar**

1. Fill small saucepan with 2.5 cm (1 inch) of water and bring to simmer over medium heat. Put chocolate in small bowl and set over simmering water. Cook, stirring, until chocolate is melted and smooth, about 5 minutes. Remove bowl from saucepan.

2. Combine chocolate, liqueur, and corn syrup in medium bowl. Whisk together powdered egg whites and warm water until egg white powder is completely dissolved, about 2 minutes. With electric mixer on low speed, beat egg white mixture until foamy. Increase speed to medium-high and beat until soft peaks form when beaters are lifted. Add sugar, 15 ml (1 Tbsp) at a time, beating until stiff, glossy peaks form when beaters are lifted.

3. With rubber spatula, stir about one-third of meringue into chocolate mixture to lighten it. Fold remaining meringue into chocolate mixture in two batches just until whites are no longer visible. Spoon mousse into serving bowl. Refrigerate, covered, until firm, at least 3 hours or up to overnight.

PER SERVING (⅛ OF MOUSSE): 38 grams, 118 Cal, 6 g Total Fat, 3 g Sat Fat, 0 g Trans Fat, 0 mg Chol, 25 mg Sod, 17 g Total Carb, 14 g Total Sugar, 1 g Fib, 2 g Prot, 0 g Alcohol, 0 g Sugar Alcohol, 2 mg Calc.

Grilled Nectarines
with Raspberry Sorbet and Berries

LEVEL Basic

PREP 15 min

GRILL 5 min

SERVES 4

▲ 4   **large nectarines, halved and pitted**

22 ml   **(1 ½ Tbsp) sugar**

1   **pint raspberry sorbet, slightly softened**

▲ 1   **170 g (6 oz) container raspberries**

4   **fresh mint sprigs**

1. Preheat grill to medium or prepare medium fire using direct method.

2. Spray cut sides of nectarines with olive oil nonstick spray and sprinkle evenly with sugar. Place nectarines, cut side down, on grill rack and grill, turning once, until slightly softened and nicely marked, about 3 minutes per side. Transfer to plate.

3. Place 2 nectarine halves on each of 4 plates. Place 60 ml (¼ cup) scoop of sorbet in each half. Scatter raspberries around nectarines and garnish each serving with mint sprig.

PER SERVING (1 DESSERT): 319 grams, 207 Cal, 1 g Total Fat, 0 g Sat Fat, 0 g Trans Fat, 0 mg Chol, 5 mg Sod, 49 g Total Carb, 41 g Total Sugar, 5 g Fib, 3 g Prot, 17 mg Calc.

FYI The **nectarines** can also be cooked in a grill pan or broiled.

5 Bonus Chapter

Don't Eat Out, Eat In

Pork Lo Mein

Pork Lo Mein

7 PointsPlus value

Per Serving

LEVEL Basic

PREP 20 min

COOK 30 min

SERVES 6

▲ **250 g** **(½ lb) wheat spaghetti**

▲ **250 ml** **(1 cup) reduced-sodium chicken broth**

30 ml **(2 Tbsp) dry sherry**

30 ml **(2 Tbsp) reduced-sodium soy sauce**

22 ml **(1 ½ Tbsp) cornstarch**

5 ml **(1 tsp) Asian (dark) sesame oil**

▲ **375 g** **(¾ lb) lean pork tenderloin, cut into thin strips**

▲ **250 g** **(½ lb) shiitake mushrooms, stemmed and caps sliced**

▲ **3** **scallions, sliced**

3 **garlic cloves, finely chopped**

1. Cook spaghetti according to package directions, omitting salt if desired; drain in colander. Rinse under cold running water; drain again. Transfer to medium bowl.

2. Meanwhile, whisk together broth, sherry, soy sauce, cornstarch, and sesame oil in small bowl until smooth.

3. Spray nonstick wok or large deep skillet with nonstick spray and set over high heat. Add pork and stir-fry until browned, about 4 minutes; transfer to plate.

4. Spray wok with nonstick spray. Add mushrooms, scallions, and garlic; stir-fry until mushrooms are softened, about 3 minutes. Re-stir broth mixture; add to wok and stir-fry until sauce bubbles and thickens, about 2 minutes. Stir in pork and spaghetti. Stir-fry until heated through, about 1 minute longer.

PER SERVING (250 ML [1 CUP]): 179 grams, 264 Cal, 4 g Total Fat, 1 g Sat Fat, 0 g Trans Fat, 38 mg Chol, 234 mg Sod, 38 g Total Carb, 3 g Total Sugar, 6 g Fib, 20 g Prot, 29 mg Calc.

FYI Because **stir-frying** requires high heat, it's best to use canola or vegetable nonstick spray (olive oil spray will start to smoke too quickly).

Living the Good Health Guidelines

Sodium, Sugar & Alcohol

▶ **Read the labels.** Most of the sodium in the diet of most Americans comes from processed foods and restaurant foods. So get in the habit of perusing the labels on packaged foods—the lower the sodium content, the better. Look for products that are labelled "low sodium," "reduced sodium," "light in sodium," "sodium-free," or "unsalted." And ask to have your restaurant meals prepared with a minimum of salt.

▶ **Budget for sweets.** There's nothing wrong with having a small sweet treat every day, but you need to account for it by adjusting the other food you eat or your portion sizes. If you prefer, you can save the calories from a daily treat and allow yourself one rich dessert a week instead.

▶ **Make your first cocktail sparkling water.** Whether you're at a party or a bar, start with club soda or sparkling water and hold the glass in your dominant hand to make nibbling a greater challenge. You'll hydrate yourself before drinking alcohol, and you'll give yourself time to settle into the scene before enjoying a cocktail.

Kung Pao Chicken

6 PointsPlus© value ™
Per Serving

LEVEL Basic

PREP 20 min

COOK 10 min

SERVES 4

▲ 175 ml	**(¾ cup) reduced-sodium chicken broth**
60 ml	**(¼ cup) rice wine**
30 ml	**(2 Tbsp) reduced-sodium soy sauce**
15 ml	**(1 Tbsp) honey**
15 ml	**(1 Tbsp) cornstarch**
10 ml	**(2 tsp) chili garlic sauce**
7 ml	**(1 ½ tsp) canola oil**
▲ 500 g	**(1 lb) chicken tenders, cut into 2.5 cm (1 inch) chunks**
▲ ½	**small red onion, chopped**
10 ml	**(2 tsp) grated peeled fresh ginger**
▲ 1 L	**(4 cups) small broccoli florets**
▲ 1	**250 ml (8 fl oz) can sliced water chestnuts, drained**

1. Whisk together broth, rice wine, soy sauce, honey, cornstarch, and chili garlic sauce in small bowl until smooth.

2. Heat nonstick wok or large deep nonstick skillet over high heat until drop of water sizzles in pan; add oil and swirl to coat pan. Add chicken and stir-fry until cooked through, about 3 minutes; transfer to plate.

3. Reduce heat to medium-high; spray wok with nonstick spray. Add onion and ginger; stir-fry until fragrant, about 30 seconds. Add broccoli and water chestnuts; stir-fry until broccoli is crisp-tender, about 2 minutes. Re-stir cornstarch mixture; add to wok along with chicken. Stir-fry until sauce bubbles and thickens, about 2 minutes longer.

PER SERVING (310 ML [1 ¼ CUPS]): 291 grams, 242 Cal, 5 g Total Fat, 1 g Sat Fat, 0 g Trans Fat, 63 mg Chol, 436 mg Sod, 19 g Total Carb, 6 g Total Sugar, 4 g Fib, 27 g Prot, 55 mg Calc.

▲ **HEALTHY EXTRA** Add 4 scallions cut into 5 cm (2 inch) lengths to the wok along with the broccoli in step 3.

Szechuan Turkey

5 PointsPlus value
Per Serving

LEVEL Basic
PREP 15 min
COOK 10 min
SERVES 4

▲ **500 g** **(1 lb) turkey cutlets, cut into thin strips**

45 ml **(3 Tbsp) hoisin sauce**

30 ml **(2 Tbsp) cornstarch**

▲ **125 ml** **(½ cup) reduced-sodium chicken broth**

15 ml **(1 Tbsp) white wine vinegar**

10 ml **(2 tsp) chili garlic sauce**

7 ml **(1 ½ tsp) canola oil**

2 **garlic cloves, minced**

1½ **teaspoons grated peeled fresh ginger**

▲ **1** **yellow bell pepper, diced**

▲ **2** **carrots, thinly sliced**

1. Stir together turkey, 15 ml (1 Tbsp) of hoisin sauce, and 15 ml (1 Tbsp) of cornstarch in medium bowl until coated evenly.

2. Whisk together remaining 30 ml (2 Tbsp) hoisin sauce, remaining 15 ml (1 Tbsp) cornstarch, the broth, vinegar, and chili garlic sauce in small bowl until blended.

3. Heat nonstick wok or large deep skillet over high heat until drop of water sizzles in pan; add oil and swirl to coat pan. Add turkey mixture and stir-fry until turkey is almost cooked through, about 2 minutes. Add garlic and ginger; stir-fry until fragrant, about 30 seconds. Add bell pepper and carrots; stir-fry until crisp-tender, about 2 minutes. Re-stir cornstarch mixture; add to wok and stir-fry until sauce bubbles and thickens and turkey is cooked through, about 2 minutes longer.

PER SERVING (250 ML [1 CUP]): 247 grams, 210 Cal, 3 g Total Fat, 0 g Sat Fat, 0 g Trans Fat, 45 mg Chol, 466 mg Sod, 16 g Total Carb, 7 g Total Sugar, 2 g Fib, 30 g Prot, 24 mg Calc.

▲ **HEALTHY EXTRA** Serve a bowl of brown rice alongside this Szechuan-style stir-fry (150 ml [²/₃ cup] of cooked brown rice with each serving will increase the *PointsPlus* value by *3*).

Shrimp with Black Bean Sauce

LEVEL Basic
PREP 15 min
COOK 10 min
SERVES 4

▲ **500 g** **(1 lb) large shrimp, peeled and deveined, tails left on if desired**

30 ml **(2 Tbsp) cornstarch**

▲ **125 ml** **(½ cup) reduced-sodium chicken broth**

30 ml **(2 Tbsp) black bean sauce**

15 ml **(1 Tbsp) reduced-sodium soy sauce**

5 ml **(1 tsp) Asian (dark) sesame oil**

1 **shallot, finely chopped**

7 ml **(1 ½ tsp) grated peeled fresh ginger**

▲ **125 g** **(¼ lb) white or cremini mushrooms, quartered**

▲ **125 g** **(¼ lb) snow peas, trimmed and halved**

▲ **1** **small yellow bell pepper, thinly sliced**

▲ **1** **carrot, thinly sliced**

1. Toss together shrimp and 15 ml (1 Tbsp) of cornstarch in medium bowl until coated evenly.

2. Whisk together broth, black bean sauce, soy sauce, and remaining 15 ml (1 Tbsp) cornstarch in small bowl until smooth.

3. Heat nonstick wok or large deep nonstick skillet over high heat until drop of water sizzles in pan; add sesame oil and swirl to coat pan. Add shrimp and stir-fry until just opaque in centre, about 2 minutes. Add shallot and ginger; stir-fry until fragrant, about 30 seconds. Add mushrooms, snow peas, bell pepper, and carrot; stir-fry until bell pepper is crisp-tender, about 2 minutes. Re-stir broth mixture; add to wok and stir-fry until sauce bubbles and thickens, about 2 minutes longer.

PER SERVING (250 ML [1 CUP]): 233 grams, 161 Cal, 3 g Total Fat, 1 g Sat Fat, 0 g Trans Fat, 168 mg Chol, 429 mg Sod, 12 g Total Carb, 3 g Total Sugar, 2 g Fib, 21 g Prot, 65 mg Calc.

 To trim fresh **snow peas**, snap off the stem end from each pod, then pull off the string and discard.

Greek Orzo and Beef Casserole

LEVEL Basic

PREP 20 min

COOK/BAKE 55 min

SERVES 6

▲ **310 ml** (1 ¼ cups) whole wheat orzo

▲ **500 g** (1 lb) ground lean beef (5% fat or less)

▲ **1** red onion, chopped

▲ **2** celery stalks, chopped

2 garlic cloves, minced

5 ml (1 tsp) dried mint

2 ml (½ tsp) dried oregano

▲ **1** 425 ml (14 ½ fl oz) can crushed tomatoes in puree

▲ **30 ml** (2 Tbsp) no-salt added tomato paste

2 ml (½ tsp) ground cinnamon

125 ml (½ cup) crumbled reduced-fat feta cheese

15 ml (1 Tbsp) grated Romano cheese

1. Preheat oven to 180°C (350°F). Spray 20 cm (8 inch) square baking dish with nonstick spray.

2. Cook orzo according to package directions, omitting salt if desired; drain in colander. Rinse under cold running water; drain again. Transfer to large bowl.

3. Meanwhile, spray large nonstick skillet with nonstick spray and set over medium-high heat. Add beef and cook, breaking it apart with wooden spoon, until browned, about 4 minutes. Transfer to orzo in bowl.

4. Spray skillet with nonstick spray. Add onion, celery, garlic, mint, and oregano; cook, stirring, until onion is softened, about 5 minutes. Add tomatoes with puree, tomato paste, and cinnamon; reduce heat and simmer until mixture is thickened, about 8 minutes. Stir in feta. Stir into beef mixture. Transfer beef mixture to prepared baking dish; sprinkle with Romano. Bake until heated through, about 25 minutes.

PER SERVING (310 ML [1 ¼ CUPS]): 223 grams, 291 Cal, 7 g Total Fat, 3 g Sat Fat, 0 g Trans Fat, 50 mg Chol, 354 mg Sod, 32 g Total Carb, 4 g Total Sugar, 5 g Fib, 25 g Prot, 95 mg Calc.

FYI This dish is equally delicious if you substitute **reduced-fat soft goat cheese** for the feta and grated Parmesan cheese for the **Romano.**

Greek Orzo and
Beef Casserole

Lamb Shish Kebabs

LEVEL Basic

PREP 20 min

GRILL 10 min

SERVES 6

10 ml	**(2 tsp) olive oil**
2	**garlic cloves, minced**
5 ml	**(1 tsp) dried oregano**
2 ml	**(½ tsp) dried rosemary, crushed**
750 g	**(1 ½ lb) boneless leg of lamb, trimmed and cut into 30 chunks**
▲ 2	**small red onions, each cut into 6 wedges**
▲ 1	**large yellow or orange bell pepper, cut into 12 pieces**
2 ml	**(½ tsp) salt**
1 ml	**(¼ tsp) black pepper**

1. Combine oil, garlic, oregano, and rosemary in large zip-close plastic bag; add lamb. Squeeze out air and seal bag; turn to coat lamb. Refrigerate, turning bag occasionally, at least 1 hour or up to overnight.

2. Spray grill rack with nonstick spray. Preheat grill to medium-high or prepare medium-high fire using direct method.

3. Remove lamb from marinade; discard marinade. Alternately thread 5 lamb chunks, 2 onion wedges, and 2 bell pepper pieces onto each of 6 (30 cm [12 inch]) metal skewers. Sprinkle with salt and pepper. Place on prepared grill rack and grill until vegetables are tender and lamb is well marked, about 5 minutes per side for medium.

PER SERVING (1 KEBAB): 117 grams, 182 Cal, 9 g Total Fat, 3 g Sat Fat, 0 g Trans Fat, 74 mg Chol, 254 mg Sod, 4 g Total Carb, 1 g Total Sugar, 1 g Fib, 20 g Prot, 21 mg Calc.

▲ **HEALTHY EXTRA** Serve these kebabs on a bed of whole wheat couscous (150 ml [²⁄₃ cup] of whole wheat couscous with each serving will increase the *PointsPlus* value by *3*).

Lemony Chicken with Potatoes

8 PointsPlus® value™

Per Serving

LEVEL Basic

PREP 15 min

ROAST 1 hr

SERVES 4

Juice of 1 lemon

3	**garlic cloves, minced**
15 ml	**(3 tsp) olive oil**
7 ml	**(1 ½ tsp) dried oregano**
2 ml	**(½ tsp) salt**
1 ml	**(¼ tsp) black pepper**
4	**170 g (6 oz) skinless bone-in chicken thighs, trimmed**
▲ **500 g**	**(1 lb) small potatoes, scrubbed and halved**
125 ml	**(½ cup) water**

1. Preheat oven to 220°C (425°F). Place rack in large roasting pan.

2. Stir together lemon juice, garlic, 5 ml (1 tsp) of oil, the oregano, 1 ml (¼ tsp) of salt, and 0.5 ml (⅛ tsp) of pepper in large bowl. Add chicken and toss to coat evenly. Let marinate in refrigerator at least 20 minutes or up to 4 hours.

3. Meanwhile, combine remaining 10 ml (2 tsp) oil, 1 ml (¼ tsp) salt, and 0.5 (⅛ tsp) pepper in medium bowl. Add potatoes and toss to coat evenly. Scatter potatoes around rack in roasting pan; roast 20 minutes.

4. Remove chicken from marinade; reserve marinade. Place chicken on rack. Stir water into marinade; pour over chicken and potatoes. Roast until potatoes are tender and instant-read thermometer inserted into thickest part of thigh (not touching bone) registers 75°C (165°F), about 40 minutes, basting with pan juices halfway through roasting time.

PER SERVING (1 CHICKEN THIGH AND ¼ OF POTATOES): 228 grams, 309 Cal, 13 g Total Fat, 3 g Sat Fat, 0 g Trans Fat, 86 mg Chol, 381 mg Sod, 21 g Total Carb, 1 g Total Sugar, 2 g Fib, 26 g Prot, 33 mg Calc.

FYI Most supermarkets sell **skinned chicken thighs**, but it's a better value if you skin them yourself: With a paring knife, make a small slice between the meat and skin to loosen the skin. Grasp the skin with a clean paper towel and pull it away from the meat. Discard the skin and paper towel.

Tandoori-Style
Chicken

Tandoori-Style Chicken

LEVEL Basic

PREP 10 min

BROIL 10 min

SERVES 6

▲ **175 ml** **(¾ cup) plain fat-free yogourt**

Juice of ½ lemon

15 ml **(1 Tbsp) paprika**

5 ml **(1 tsp) grated peeled fresh ginger**

1 **garlic clove, minced**

5 ml **(1 tsp) ground cumin**

▲ **6** **125 g (¼ lb) chicken cutlets**

30 ml **(2 Tbsp) chopped fresh cilantro**

1. Combine yogourt, lemon juice, paprika, ginger, garlic, and cumin in large zip-close plastic bag; add chicken. Squeeze out air and seal bag; turn to coat chicken. Refrigerate at least 4 hours or up to overnight.

2. Spray broiler rack with nonstick spray. Preheat broiler.

3. Remove chicken from marinade; discard marinade. Place chicken on prepared broiler rack. Broil chicken 12.5 cm (5 inches) from heat until cooked through, about 4 minutes per side. Serve sprinkled with cilantro.

PER SERVING (1 CHICKEN CUTLET): 111 grams, 147 Cal, 3 g Total Fat, 1 g Sat Fat, 0 g Trans Fat, 63 mg Chol, 80 mg Sod, 4 g Total Carb, 2 g Total Sugar, 1 g Fib, 25 g Prot, 78 mg Calc.

▲ **HEALTHY EXTRA** Serve this chicken with a sliced cucumber and radish salad sprinkled with dill, lemon juice, and black pepper along with 15 ml (1 Tbsp) or two of plain fat-free yogourt for each serving.

Fish and Sweet Onion Vindaloo

4
PointsPlus©
value
Per Serving

LEVEL Basic
PREP 20 min
COOK 20 min
SERVES 6

10 ml   **(2 tsp) canola oil**

▲ 1   **sweet onion, chopped**

2   **garlic cloves, minced**

10 ml   **(2 tsp) grated peeled fresh ginger**

10 ml   **(2 tsp) curry powder**

▲ 750 g   **(1 ½ lb) plum tomatoes, diced**

   Juice of ½ lemon

2 ml   **(½ tsp) salt**

▲ 6   **150 g (5 oz) cod or pollock fillets, skinned**

1. Heat oil in large nonstick skillet over medium-high heat. Add onion and cook, stirring, until golden, about 7 minutes. Add garlic, ginger, and curry powder; cook, stirring, until fragrant, about 30 seconds. Stir in tomatoes, lemon juice, and salt; cook, covered, until tomatoes are softened, about 5 minutes.

2. Add cod, skinned side up, to skillet; spoon sauce over fish. Reduce heat and simmer, covered, until fish is just opaque in centre, about 8 minutes, basting with sauce halfway through cooking time.

PER SERVING (1 COD FILLET WITH ABOUT 60 ML [¼ CUP] SAUCE): 275 grams, 160 Cal, 3 g Total Fat, 0 g Sat Fat, 0 g Trans Fat, 54 mg Chol, 281 mg Sod, 10 g Total Carb, 6 g Total Sugar, 2 g Fib, 24 g Prot, 42 mg Calc.

FYI If top-quality fresh plum tomatoes are not available, use a 796 ml (28 fl oz) can of no-salt added diced tomatoes, drained, in step 1. Cook, uncovered, until the flavours are blended, about 4 minutes.

Vegetable Dal

LEVEL Basic

PREP 15 min

COOK 35 min

SERVES 4

▲ 1   **Yukon Gold potato, scrubbed and cut into 1.25 cm (½ inch) pieces**

▲ 60 ml   **(¼ cup) red lentils, picked over, rinsed, and drained**

15 ml   **(1 Tbsp) canola oil**

▲ 1   **red onion, chopped**

▲ 1   **jalapeño pepper, seeded and minced**

10 ml   **(2 tsp) curry powder**

▲ 1   **475 ml (15 ½ fl oz) can chickpeas, rinsed and drained**

▲ 1   **425 ml (14 ½ fl oz) can diced tomatoes**

2   **garlic cloves, minced**

7 ml   **(1 ½ tsp) grated peeled fresh ginger**

30 ml   **(2 Tbsp) chopped fresh cilantro**

1. Put potato in large saucepan and add enough water to cover; bring to boil. Reduce heat and cook until potato is almost tender, about 7 minutes. With slotted spoon, transfer potato to medium bowl.

2. Add lentils to cooking liquid in saucepan; bring to boil. Reduce heat and cook, uncovered, until lentils are tender but still hold their shape, about 8 minutes; drain.

3. Heat oil in large nonstick skillet over medium-high heat. Add onion, jalapeño, and curry powder. Cook until onion is softened, about 5 minutes. Stir in potato, chickpeas, tomatoes, garlic, and ginger. Cook, stirring occasionally, until potato is tender, about 5 minutes. Stir in lentils and cook until heated through, about 1 minute longer. Remove saucepan from heat and stir in cilantro.

PER SERVING (250 ML [1 CUP]): 351 grams, 263 Cal, 5 g Total Fat, 0 g Sat Fat, 0 g Trans Fat, 0 mg Chol, 474 mg Sod, 45 g Total Carb, 8 g Total Sugar, 9 g Fib, 10 g Prot, 60 mg Calc.

 If the dal is a bit too thick, stir in a little reduced-sodium vegetable broth or water until the desired consistency.

Pork Piccata

6
PointsPlus®
value
™
Per Serving

LEVEL Basic
PREP 10 min
COOK 10 min
SERVES 4

125 ml	(½ cup) Italian-seasoned dried bread crumbs
▲ 60 ml	(¼ cup) fat-free egg substitute
30 ml	(2 Tbsp) whole grain mustard
▲ 4	125 g (¼ lb) boneless lean pork loin chops, trimmed and pounded to 0.5 cm (¼ inch) thickness
10 ml	(2 tsp) extra-virgin olive oil
▲ 30 ml	(2 Tbsp) reduced-sodium chicken broth
	Juice of ½ lemon
15 ml	(1 Tbsp) finely chopped fresh parsley

1. Spread bread crumbs on sheet of wax paper. Beat egg substitute and mustard in large shallow bowl or pie plate. Working with 1 piece of pork at a time, dip into egg mixture, then coat with bread crumbs, pressing lightly so they adhere. Transfer to large plate.

2. Heat oil in large nonstick skillet over medium heat. Add pork and cook until golden and cooked through, about 5 minutes per side. Transfer pork to platter; keep warm.

3. To make sauce, whisk broth and lemon juice into skillet; simmer 30 seconds. Stir in parsley. Pour sauce over pork.

PER SERVING (1 PORK CUTLET WITH ABOUT 15 ML [1 TBSP] SAUCE): 132 grams, 225 Cal, 9 g Total Fat, 2 g Sat Fat, 0 g Trans Fat, 66 mg Chol, 320 mg Sod, 11 g Total Carb, 1 g Total Sugar, 1 g Fib, 25 g Prot, 46 mg Calc.

FYI **Pounding the pork to an even thickness** ensures that the meat cooks uniformly. The easiest way to do this is to place the pork between two pieces of plastic wrap, leaving room around each chop. Then, with a meat mallet, rolling pin, or bottom of a small heavy saucepan, pound the meat to the desired thickness.

Risotto with Sausage and Greens

PointsPlus value

Per Serving

LEVEL Intermediate

PREP 15 min

COOK 40 min

SERVES 6

250 g	(½ lb) sweet Italian-style chicken sausage, casings removed and sausage broken up
▲ ½	bunch broccoli rabe, trimmed and chopped
▲ 750 ml	(3 cups) reduced-sodium chicken broth
10 ml	(2 tsp) extra-virgin olive oil
2	shallots, minced
310 ml	(1 ¼ cups) Arborio or other short-grain white rice
75 ml	(⅓ cup) dry vermouth
1 ml	(¼ tsp) black pepper

1. Spray large nonstick skillet with nonstick spray and set over medium heat. Add sausage and cook, stirring occasionally, until lightly browned, about 5 minutes. Stir in broccoli rabe; cook, covered, until broccoli rabe is tender and sausage is cooked through, about 7 minutes. Remove skillet from heat.

2. Meanwhile, bring broth to boil in medium saucepan. Reduce heat and keep at gentle simmer.

3. Heat oil in nonstick Dutch oven over medium heat. Add shallots and cook, stirring occasionally, until softened, about 3 minutes. Add rice and cook, stirring frequently, until lightly toasted, about 3 minutes. Add vermouth and cook, stirring frequently, until almost absorbed, about 1 minute. Add simmering broth, 125 ml (½ cup) at a time, stirring until broth is absorbed before adding more; cook until rice is tender but still chewy in centre. Add sausage mixture and pepper; cook, stirring frequently, just until heated through, about 1 minute longer.

PER SERVING (250 ML [1 CUP]): 262 grams, 253 Cal, 5 g Total Fat, 1 g Sat Fat, 0 g Trans Fat, 29 mg Chol, 492 mg Sod, 36 g Total Carb, 1 g Total Sugar, 2 g Fib, 13 g Prot, 31 mg Calc.

▲ **HEALTHY EXTRA** Start your meal with a tasty sliced mushroom and baby arugula salad dressed with lemon juice.

Lasagna Bolognese

8 PointsPlus value Per Serving

LEVEL Intermediate

PREP 25 min

COOK/BAKE 1 hr 10 min

SERVES 6

▲ **9** — whole wheat lasagna noodles

▲ **250 g** — **(½ lb) ground skinless turkey breast**

▲ **1** — **onion, chopped**

▲ **1** — **orange or yellow bell pepper, diced**

▲ **1** — **zucchini, diced**

5 ml — **(1 tsp) fennel seeds, finely crushed**

▲ **2** — **500 ml (16 fl oz) jars fat-free marinara sauce**

▲ **375 ml** — **(1 ½ cups) fat-free ricotta cheese**

175 ml — **(¾ cup) shredded low-fat Italian cheese blend**

1. Preheat oven to 190°C (375°F). Spray 22 x 33 cm (9 x13 inch) baking dish with nonstick spray.

2. Cook noodles according to package directions, omitting salt if desired; drain in colander. Rinse under cold running water; drain again.

3. Meanwhile, to make sauce, spray large nonstick skillet with nonstick spray and set over medium-high heat. Add turkey, onion, bell pepper, zucchini, and fennel seeds. Cook, breaking turkey apart with wooden spoon, until browned and pan juices are evaporated, about 10 minutes.

4. Stir marinara sauce into skillet and bring to boil. Reduce heat and simmer until sauce is slightly thickened and flavours are blended, about 10 minutes.

5. Spread one-fourth of sauce in prepared baking dish. Top with 3 noodles; spread 125 ml (½ cup) of ricotta over noodles. Repeat layering with sauce, noodles, and ricotta two times; top with remaining sauce. Cover dish with foil and bake 30 minutes. Uncover and sprinkle cheese blend over lasagna. Bake, uncovered, until heated through and cheeses are lightly browned, about 20 minutes longer. Let stand 10 minutes before serving.

PER SERVING (⅙ OF LASAGNA): 393 grams, 355 Cal, 3 g Total Fat, 1 g Sat Fat, 0 g Trans Fat, 23 mg Chol, 837 mg Sod, 49 g Total Carb, 6 g Total Sugar, 11 g Fib, 32 g Prot, 331 mg Calc.

FYI To finely crush the **fennel**, loosely wrap the seeds in a clean kitchen towel and pound with a rolling pin or a small heavy saucepan.

Lasagna Bolognese

Shrimp Scampi

3 PointsPlus® value™

Per Serving

LEVEL Basic

PREP 20 min

COOK/BROIL 10 min

SERVES 4

▲ **500 g** **(1 lb) large shrimp, peeled**

20 ml **(4 tsp) unsalted butter**

2 **shallots, minced**

1 **garlic clove, minced**

Juice of ½ lemon

2 ml **(½ tsp) salt**

Pinch red pepper flakes

30 ml **(2 Tbsp) chopped fresh parsley**

1. To butterfly shrimp, with small knife, cut along curved back of each shrimp almost, but not completely, through. With tip of knife, lift out dark vein. Open each shrimp and press down to slightly flatten.

2. Melt butter in large nonstick skillet over medium heat. Add shallots and garlic; cook, stirring, until shallots are golden, about 5 minutes. Remove skillet from heat; stir in lemon juice, salt, and pepper flakes. Add shrimp and toss to coat.

3. Preheat broiler. Arrange shrimp in single layer in shallow flameproof baking dish. Broil 12.5 cm (5 inches) from heat until lightly browned and just opaque in centre, about 3 minutes per side. Serve sprinkled with parsley.

PER SERVING (6 SHRIMP): 115 grams, 133 Cal, 5 g Total Fat, 3 g Sat Fat, 0 g Trans Fat, 178 mg Chol, 487 mg Sod, 3 g Total Carb, 1 g Total Sugar, 0 g Fib, 19 g Prot, 45 mg Calc.

▲ **HEALTHY EXTRA** Enjoy these garlicky shrimp with a side of steamed whole green beans and brown rice (150 ml [⅔ cup] of cooked brown rice with each serving will increase the *PointsPlus* value by *3*).

Turkey-Vegetable Noodle Bowl

LEVEL Basic

PREP 15 min

COOK 20 min

SERVES 6

125 g	**(¼ lb) multigrain linguine**
2	**garlic cloves, minced**
7 ml	**(1 ½ tsp) grated peeled fresh ginger**
▲ 500 g	**(1 lb) turkey cutlets, cut into thin strips**
▲ 1	**1 L (32 fl oz) carton reduced-sodium chicken broth**
45 ml	**(3 Tbsp) sake or dry sherry**
30 ml	**(2 Tbsp) reduced-sodium soy sauce**
▲ 125 g	**(¼ lb) shiitake mushrooms, stemmed and caps sliced**
▲ 6	**scallions, sliced**
▲ 1	**carrot, thinly sliced**
60 ml	**(¼ cup) lightly packed fresh cilantro leaves**

1. Cook linguine according to package directions, omitting salt if desired.

2. Meanwhile, spray nonstick Dutch oven with nonstick spray and set over medium-high heat. Add garlic and ginger; cook, stirring, until fragrant, about 30 seconds. Stir in turkey.

3. Add broth, sake, and soy sauce to turkey mixture; bring to boil. Reduce heat and simmer, covered, until turkey is cooked through, about 10 minutes. Stir in mushrooms, scallions, and carrot. Cook, covered, until vegetables are tender, about 5 minutes. Add linguine, tossing to mix well. Divide evenly among 6 soup bowls and sprinkle with cilantro.

PER SERVING (GENEROUS 250 ML [1 CUP]):
305 grams, 192 Cal, 1 g Total Fat, 0 g Sat Fat, 0 g Trans Fat, 30 mg Chol, 558 mg Sod, 21 g Total Carb, 3 g Total Sugar, 4 g Fib, 25 g Prot, 37 mg Calc.

▲ **HEALTHY EXTRA** A bowl of edamame is a great way to whet your appetite for this dish (125 ml [1 ½ cup] of cooked shelled edamame for each serving will increase the *PointsPlus* value by *2*).

Lean Protein

▶ **Make meat the side dish.** Instead of letting it take centre stage, move a fist-size skinless chicken breast or piece of steak or lamb to a corner of your plate and fill the rest with veggies and salads. This strategy ensures that you get enough lean protein but not too much—and it keeps a meal's calories under control.

▶ **Try a new bird.** Don't get stuck in a chicken rut; treat your taste buds to Cornish game hen, duck, turkey, or capon. They're all easy to cook, affordable, and delicious hot or cold.

▶ **Take the alternative route.** Your protein intake doesn't have to consist entirely of meat, poultry, or fish. Go vegetarian a few meals a week, using tofu, tempeh, eggs, lentils, or beans as your primary protein source. Similarly, keep hard-cooked eggs in the fridge for a quick, protein-rich snack.

Salmon and Vegetable Teriyaki

Per Serving

LEVEL Basic

PREP 20 min

COOK/BROIL 15 min

SERVES 4

75 ml	(⅓ cup) sake or dry sherry
45 ml	(3 Tbsp) reduced-sodium soy sauce
4	125 g (¼ lb) skinless salmon fillets
2	garlic cloves, minced
10 ml	(2 tsp) grated peeled fresh ginger
▲ 2	different colour bell peppers, thinly sliced
▲ 250 ml	(1 cup) snow peas, trimmed and cut crosswise in half
▲ 1	carrot, cut into matchstick strips

1. To make teriyaki sauce, bring sake and soy sauce to boil in small saucepan. Reduce heat and simmer until sauce is reduced to 60 ml (¼ cup), about 5 minutes. Remove pan from heat.

2. Spray broiler rack with nonstick spray. Preheat broiler.

3. Place salmon on prepared broiler rack. Broil 12.5 cm (5 inches) from heat just until opaque in centre, about 4 minutes per side, brushing with 30 ml (2 Tbsp) of sauce halfway through broiling time.

4. Meanwhile, spray large nonstick skillet with nonstick spray and set over medium-high heat. Add garlic and ginger; cook, stirring constantly, until fragrant, about 30 seconds. Add bell peppers, snow peas, and carrot; cook, stirring frequently, until vegetables are crisp-tender, about 4 minutes longer.

5. Drizzle vegetables with remaining 30 ml (2 Tbsp) sauce. Serve with salmon.

PER SERVING (1 SALMON FILLET WITH 125 ML [½ CUP] VEGETABLES): 226 grams, 250 Cal, 9 g Total Fat, 1 g Sat Fat, 0 g Trans Fat, 72 mg Chol, 363 mg Sod, 8 g Total Carb, 3 g Total Sugar, 2 g Fib, 28 g Prot, 37 mg Calc.

FYI **Double or triple the teriyaki sauce** and use the extra for broiled steaks, poultry, or vegetables. It will keep indefinitely in the refrigerator.

Vegetarian Soba Salad

Vegetarian Soba Salad

8 PointsPlus® value
Per Serving

LEVEL Basic

PREP 15 min

COOK 20 min

SERVES 5

250 g	(½ lb) soba noodles
30 ml	(2 Tbsp) mirin or dry sherry
15 ml	(1 Tbsp) rice vinegar
15 ml	(Tbsp) reduced-sodium soy sauce
5 ml	(1 tsp) Asian (dark) sesame oil
1	garlic clove, minced
2 ml	(½ tsp) grated peeled fresh ginger
▲ 125 g	(¼ lb) sugar snap peas, trimmed and cut crosswise in half
▲ 1	420 g (14 oz) package extra-firm tofu, drained and cut into 2.5 cm (1 inch) cubes
▲ 1	red bell pepper, thinly sliced
▲ 4	scallions, thinly sliced

1. Cook noodles according to package directions. With tongs, transfer noodles to colander; drain; reserving cooking liquid. Rinse noodles under cold running water; drain again. Transfer to large bowl.

2. To make dressing, whisk together mirin, vinegar, soy sauce, sesame oil, garlic, and ginger in small bowl.

3. Return cooking liquid to boil. Add sugar snap peas and boil just until bright green, about 2 minutes. Drain in colander. Rinse under cold running water; drain again.

4. Add tofu, bell pepper, scallions, and sugar snap peas to noodles in bowl. Drizzle with dressing and gently toss to coat. Serve at room temperature or refrigerate to serve chilled.

PER SERVING (ABOUT 250 ML [1 CUP]): 198 grams, 268 Cal, 6 g Total Fat, 0 g Sat Fat, 0 g Trans Fat, 0 mg Chol, 442 mg Sod, 42 g Total Carb, 4 g Total Sugar, 2 g Fib, 15 g Prot, 189 mg Calc.

▲ **HEALTHY EXTRA** End the meal with a fruit salad of fresh lychees, sliced kiwi, and halved strawberries.

Scallop and Bell Pepper Stir-Fry

7 PointsPlus® value
Per Serving

LEVEL Basic

PREP 15 min

COOK 10 min

SERVES 4

▲ **500 g** **(1 lb) sea scallops**

2 **garlic cloves, minced**

5 ml **(1 tsp) grated peeled fresh ginger**

▲ **250 g** **(½ lb) asparagus, cut into 3.5 cm (1 ½ inch) lengths**

▲ **2** **different colour bell peppers, thinly sliced**

▲ **1** **small onion, thinly sliced**

▲ **1** **carrot, cut into matchstick strips**

30 ml **(2 Tbsp) dry sherry**

15 ml **(1 Tbsp) reduced-sodium soy sauce**

▲ **500 ml** **(2 cups) hot cooked brown rice**

1. Pat scallops dry with paper towels. Spray nonstick wok or large deep skillet with nonstick spray and set over high heat. Add scallops and stir-fry until browned but still slightly translucent in centre, about 2 minutes. Transfer to plate; keep warm.

2. Spray wok with nonstick spray. Add garlic and ginger; stir-fry until fragrant, about 30 seconds. Add asparagus, bell peppers, onion, and carrot; stir-fry until vegetables are crisp-tender, about 4 minutes.

3. Stir in sherry and soy sauce; bring to boil. Boil, stirring, until flavours are blended, about 30 seconds. Return scallops to wok and stir-fry just until heated through, about 1 minute longer. Serve with rice.

PER SERVING (310 ML [1 ¼ CUPS] SCALLOP MIXTURE AND 125 ML [½ CUP] RICE): 346 grams, 310 Cal, 2 g Total Fat, 0 g Sat Fat, 0 g Trans Fat, 66 mg Chol, 517 mg Sod, 39 g Total Carb, 5 g Total Sugar, 5 g Fib, 32 g Prot, 80 mg Calc.

FYI If you see a white strip (muscle) along the short edge of a **scallop**, remove it before cooking. Although the muscle is edible, it's the toughest part of the scallop.

Tex-Mex Chef's Salad

LEVEL Basic
PREP 20 min
BAKE/COOK 20 min
SERVES 4

3	**15 cm (6 inch) corn tortillas, each cut into 8 wedges**
▲ 1	**red onion, chopped**
2	**garlic cloves, minced**
375 g	**(¾ lb) ground lean pork**
45 ml	**(3 Tbsp) salt-free fajita seasoning**
60 ml	**(¼ cup) water**
▲ 125 ml	**(½ cup) canned reduced-sodium black beans, rinsed and drained**
▲ 125 ml	**(½ cup) canned Mexican-style corn, drained**
60 ml	**(¼ cup) chopped fresh cilantro**
▲ 750 ml	**(3 cups) lightly packed baby spinach**
▲ 1	**tomato, diced**

1. Preheat oven to 200°C (400°F). Spray large nonstick baking sheet with nonstick spray.

2. Arrange tortillas on prepared baking sheet in single layer; lightly spray with nonstick spray. Bake tortillas, turning occasionally, until crisp and edges begin to curl slightly, about 10 minutes. Transfer baking sheet to rack and let cool completely.

3. Meanwhile, spray large nonstick skillet with nonstick spray and set over medium heat. Add onion and garlic; cook, stirring, until onion is golden, about 7 minutes. Add pork and fajita seasoning; cook, breaking pork apart with wooden spoon, until lightly browned, about 8 minutes. Stir in water. Increase heat to medium-high and cook, stirring occasionally, until water is evaporated, about 3 minutes. Add beans, corn, and cilantro; cook, stirring, until heated through, about 1 minute.

4. Line large platter with spinach. Top with pork mixture and tomato. Tuck tortilla chips into pork mixture.

PER SERVING (ABOUT 175 ML [¾ CUP] SPINACH, 175 ML [¾ CUP] PORK MIXTURE, AND 6 TORTILLA CHIPS): 230 grams, 249 Cal, 7 g Total Fat, 2 g Sat Fat, 0 g Trans Fat, 42 mg Chol, 249 mg Sod, 26 g Total Carb, 4 g Total Sugar, 4 g Fib, 20 g Prot, 47 mg Calc.

 FYI Give this salad a **dose of extra heat** by sprinkling the tortillas with chili powder before baking them in step 2.

Easy Chimichangas

7 PointsPlus value

Per Serving

LEVEL Basic
PREP 15 min
COOK/BAKE 35 min
SERVES 4

▲ **250 g** **(½ lb) ground lean beef (5% fat or less)**

▲ **1** **onion, finely chopped**

1 **garlic clove, minced**

10 ml **(2 tsp) chili powder**

5 ml **(1 tsp) dried oregano**

▲ **1** **250 ml (8 fl oz) can no-salt added tomato sauce**

75 ml **(⅓ cup) shredded reduced-fat pepper Jack cheese**

4 **20 cm (8 inch) whole wheat flour tortillas, warmed**

1. Preheat oven to 200°C (400°F). Lightly spray nonstick baking sheet with nonstick spray.

2. To make filling, spray medium nonstick skillet with nonstick spray and set over medium-high heat. Add beef, onion, garlic, chili powder, and oregano; cook, breaking beef apart with wooden spoon, until browned, about 6 minutes. Stir in tomato sauce and bring to boil. Reduce heat and simmer until flavours are blended and mixture is slightly thickened, about 5 minutes. Remove skillet from heat and stir in pepper Jack.

3. Spoon about 125 ml (½ cup) of filling down centre of each tortilla. Fold in sides and roll up to enclose filling. Place chimichangas, seam side down, on prepared baking sheet. Lightly spray tops with nonstick spray. Bake until crisp and golden, about 20 minutes.

PER SERVING (1 CHIMICHANGA): 191 grams, 283 Cal, 8 g Total Fat, 3 g Sat Fat, 0 g Trans Fat, 39 mg Chol, 300 mg Sod, 31 g Total Carb, 6 g Total Sugar, 4 g Fib, 19 g Prot, 164 mg Calc.

▲ **HEALTHY EXTRA** Serve the chimichangas topped with chopped fresh tomatoes, sliced scallions, and chopped fresh parsley.

Easy Chimichangas

Turkey Chili with Black Beans

6 PointsPlus® value™ Per Serving

LEVEL Basic

PREP 15 min

COOK 1 hr 25 min

SERVES 6

▲ 1   **large red onion, chopped**

▲ 1   **125 ml (4 fl oz) can chopped mild green chiles**

3   **garlic cloves, minced**

30 ml   **(2 Tbsp) chili powder**

30 ml   **(2 Tbsp) salt-free Creole seasoning**

▲ 500 g   **(1 lb) ground skinless turkey breast**

▲ 2   **425 ml (14 ½ fl oz) cans no-salt added diced tomatoes**

▲ 250 ml   **(1 cup) fat-free salsa**

125 ml   **(½ cup) water**

▲ 2   **475 ml (15 ½ fl oz) cans reduced-sodium black beans, rinsed and drained**

1. Spray nonstick Dutch oven with nonstick spray and set over medium heat. Add onion and cook, stirring, until softened, about 5 minutes. Add chiles, garlic, chili powder, and Creole seasoning; cook, stirring, until fragrant, about 1 minute. Add turkey and cook, breaking it apart with wooden spoon, until browned about 8 minutes.

2. Stir tomatoes, salsa, and water into turkey mixture; bring to boil. Reduce heat and simmer, covered, until flavours are blended and chili is slightly thickened, about 1 hour. Stir in beans and cook until heated through, about 3 minutes longer.

PER SERVING (325 ML [1 ⅓ CUPS]): 465 grams, 230 Cal, 2 g Total Fat, 0 g Sat Fat, 0 g Trans Fat, 30 mg Chol, 602 mg Sod, 34 g Total Carb, 9 g Total Sugar, 10 g Fib, 26 g Prot, 82 mg Calc.

▲ **HEALTHY EXTRA** Serve this chili with shredded cheese (30 g [1 oz] of fat-free Cheddar cheese with each serving will increase the *PointsPlus* value by *1*).

Thai Steak Skewers

LEVEL Basic

PREP 25 min

GRILL 5 min

SERVES 4

▲ **60 ml** **(¼ cup) finely chopped red onion**

30 ml **(2 Tbsp) honey**

15 ml **(1 Tbsp) finely chopped fresh lemongrass**

▲ **1** **jalapeño pepper, seeded and minced**

2 **garlic cloves, minced**

10 ml **(2 tsp) grated peeled fresh ginger**

10 ml **(2 tsp) reduced-sodium soy sauce**

10 ml **(2 tsp) Asian fish sauce**

5 ml **(1 tsp) Asian (dark) sesame oil**

▲ **1** **500 g (1 lb) top round steak, trimmed and cut into ¼-inch slices**

▲ **2** **scallions, finely chopped**

30 ml **(2 Tbsp) finely chopped unsalted peanuts**

1. Combine onion, honey, lemongrass, jalapeño, garlic, ginger, soy sauce, fish sauce, and sesame oil in large zip-close plastic bag; add steak. Squeeze out air and seal bag; turn to coat steak. Refrigerate, turning bag occasionally, at least 1 hour or up to overnight.

2. Spray grill rack with nonstick spray. Preheat grill to medium-high or prepare medium-high fire using direct method.

3. Remove steak from marinade. Scrape off any excess marinade and discard. Thread steak onto 8 (20 cm [8 inch]) metal skewers. Place on grill rack and grill until beef is well marked, about 3 minutes per side for medium. Sprinkle with scallions and peanuts.

PER SERVING (2 SKEWERS): 131 grams, 242 Cal, 8 g Total Fat, 2 g Sat Fat, 0 g Trans Fat, 65 mg Chol, 335 mg Sod, 12 g Total Carb, 10 g Total Sugar, 1 g Fib, 29 g Prot, 22 mg Calc.

 FYI No fresh lemongrass on hand? Substitute the grated zest of 1 lemon.

Beef, Tomato, and Peanut Salad

4 PointsPlus® value

Per Serving

LEVEL Basic

PREP 20 min

COOK None

SERVES 6

45 ml	**(3 Tbsp) lime juice**
15 ml	**(1 Tbsp) brown sugar**
10 ml	**(2 tsp) Asian fish sauce**
2 ml	**(½ tsp) Thai red curry paste**
▲ 375 g	**(¾ lb) thinly sliced fat-free roast beef, cut into thin strips**
▲ ½	**small orange or yellow bell pepper, diced**
▲ 2	**plum tomatoes, chopped**
▲ 1	**small onion, thinly sliced**
▲ 1	**small cucumber, peeled, halved, and thinly sliced**
60 ml	**(¼ cup) coarsely chopped fresh cilantro**
60 ml	**(¼ cup) coarsely chopped fresh mint**
▲ 6	**large butter lettuce leaves**
60 ml	**(¼ cup) unsalted peanuts, finely chopped**
	Lime wedges

1. To make dressing, whisk together lime juice, brown sugar, fish sauce, and curry paste in small bowl.

2. Toss together roast beef, bell pepper, tomato, onion, cucumber, cilantro, and mint in large bowl. Add dressing and toss to coat evenly.

3. Place lettuce on platter; top with roast beef mixture. Sprinkle evenly with peanuts and serve with lime wedges.

PER SERVING (⅙ OF SALAD): 167 grams, 141 Cal, 5 g Total Fat, 1 g Sat Fat, 0 g Trans Fat, 27 mg Chol, 744 mg Sod, 12 g Total Carb, 7 g Total Sugar, 2 g Fib, 14 g Prot, 28 mg Calc.

▲ **HEALTHY EXTRA** Add 1 carrot, grated, to the salad in step 2.

Chicken and Rice Salad

LEVEL Basic

PREP 15 min

COOK 20 min

SERVES 6

▲ **250 ml (1 cup) brown basmati rice**

45 ml (3 Tbsp) chopped fresh mint

Juice of 1 large lime

15 ml (1 Tbsp) unseasoned rice vinegar

10 ml (2 tsp) Asian (dark) sesame oil

1 ml (¼ tsp) hot pepper sauce

▲ **500 ml (2 cups) lightly packed spinach, coarsely chopped**

▲ **250 ml (1 cup) mung bean sprouts**

▲ **½ small red onion, diced**

▲ **175 ml (¾ cup) thinly sliced cooked skinless chicken breast**

1. Cook rice according to package directions; fluff with fork. Transfer to serving bowl and let cool completely.

2. Meanwhile, to make dressing, whisk together mint, lime juice, vinegar, sesame oil, and pepper sauce in small bowl.

3. Add spinach, bean sprouts, and onion to rice in bowl. Drizzle with half of dressing and toss to coat evenly. Top with chicken and drizzle with remaining dressing.

PER SERVING (250 ML [1 CUP]): 96 grams, 150 Cal, 2 g Total Fat, 0 g Sat Fat, 0 g Trans Fat, 15 mg Chol, 35 mg Sod, 27 g Total Carb, 2 g Total Sugar, 2 g Fib, 9 g Prot, 19 mg Calc.

FYI Crunchy with a hint of sweetness, **mung bean sprouts** are perfect for salads. Look for plump sprouts that are not stringy or discoloured. Mung bean sprouts may be refrigerated in a zip-close plastic bag for up to 2 days.

Ginger Shrimp and Vegetables

Ginger Shrimp and Vegetables

LEVEL Basic

PREP 15 min

COOK 10 min

SERVES 4

10 ml	**(2 tsp) canola oil**
▲ 500 g	**(1 lb) peeled and deveined large shrimp**
2	**garlic cloves, minced**
7 ml	**(1 ½ tsp) grated peeled fresh ginger**
▲ 2	**red bell peppers, thinly sliced**
▲ 250 ml	**(1 cup) snow peas, trimmed and halved**
▲ 1	**carrot, shredded**
30 ml	**(2 Tbsp) light (low-fat) coconut milk**
10 ml	**(2 tsp) brown sugar**
10 ml	**(2 tsp) reduced-sodium soy sauce**
▲ 500 ml	**(2 cups) hot cooked brown rice**

1. Heat nonstick wok or deep large nonstick skillet over medium-high heat until drop of water sizzles in pan; add 5 ml (1 tsp) of oil and swirl to coat pan. Add shrimp and stir-fry until just opaque in centre, about 3 minutes. Transfer to plate; keep warm.

2. Heat remaining 5 ml (1 tsp) oil in wok. Add garlic and ginger; stir-fry until fragrant, about 30 seconds. Add bell peppers, snow peas, and carrot; stir-fry until vegetables are crisp-tender, about 3 minutes. Stir in coconut milk, brown sugar, and soy sauce; stir-fry until sugar is dissolved, about 30 seconds. Stir in shrimp and toss until heated through, about 1 minute longer. Serve with rice.

PER SERVING (ABOUT 250 ML [1 CUP] SHRIMP WITH VEGETABLES AND 125 ML [½ CUP] RICE): 291 grams, 267 Cal, 5 g Total Fat, 1 g Sat Fat, 0 g Trans Fat, 168 mg Chol, 274 mg Sod, 33 g Total Carb, 6 g Total Sugar, 4 g Fib, 22 g Prot, 64 mg Calc.

FYI When **grating fresh ginger**, for best results, use the small holes of a box grater. A 1.25 cm (½ inch) piece of ginger will yield about 7 ml (1 ½ tsp) of grated ginger.

Chunky Guacamole, page 140

Index

Dry and Liquid Measurement Equivalents

TEASPOONS	TABLESPOONS	CUPS	FLUID OUNCES
3 teaspoons	1 tablespoon		½ fluid ounce
6 teaspoons	2 tablespoons	⅛ cup	1 fluid ounce
8 teaspoons	2 tablespoons plus 2 teaspoons	⅙ cup	
12 teaspoons	4 tablespoons	¼ cup	2 fluid ounces
15 teaspoons	5 tablespoons	⅓ cup minus 1 teaspoon	
16 teaspoons	5 tablespoons plus 1 teaspoon	⅓ cup	
18 teaspoons	6 tablespoons	¼ cup plus 2 tablespoons	3 fluid ounces
24 teaspoons	8 tablespoons	½ cup	4 fluid ounces
30 teaspoons	10 tablespoons	½ cup plus 2 tablespoons	5 fluid ounces
32 teaspoons	10 tablespoons plus 2 teaspoons	⅔ cup	
36 teaspoons	12 tablespoons	¾ cup	6 fluid ounces
42 teaspoons	14 tablespoons	1 cup minus 2 tablespoons	7 fluid ounces
45 teaspoons	15 tablespoons	1 cup minus 1 tablespoon	
48 teaspoons	16 tablespoons	1 cup	8 fluid ounces

VOLUME	
¼ teaspoon	1 millilitre
½ teaspoon	2 milliliters
1 teaspoon	5 millilitres
1 tablespoon	15 millilitres
2 tablespoons	30 millilitres
3 tablespoons	45 millilitres
¼ cup	60 millilitres
⅓ cup	75 millilitres
½ cup	125 millilitres
⅔ cup	150 millilitres
¾ cup	175 millilitres
1 cup	250 millilitres
1 quart	1 litre

LENGTH	
1 inch	25 millimetres
1 inch	2.5 centimetres

WEIGHT	
1 ounce	30 grams
¼ pound	125 grams
½ pound	250 grams
1 pound	500 grams

OVEN TEMPERATURE			
250°F	120°C	400°F	200°C
275°F	140°C	425°F	220°C
300°F	150°C	450°F	230°C
325°F	160°C	475°F	250°C
350°F	180°C	500°F	260°C
375°F	190°C	525°F	270°C

Note: Measurement of less than .5ml (⅛ teaspoon) is considered a dash or a pinch. Metric volume measurements are approximate.